COMBAT INTELLIGENCE
IN
MODERN WARFARE

To know is to conquer.

Not to know is to risk sudden destruction.

COMBAT INTELLIGENCE
IN
MODERN WARFARE

By
IRVING HEYMONT
Lieutenant Colonel, U.S. Army

Knowledge is Power

THE BEST IN MILITARY BOOKS

MILITARY SERVICE DIVISION
THE STACKPOLE COMPANY
Harrisburg, Pennsylvania

The Military Service Publishing Company,
pre-eminent for more than a quarter of a century in
publishing military texts, continues as *Military Service
Division* of The Stackpole Company. Under the same
management and editorial staff as before, it will spare
no effort in providing
THE BEST IN MILITARY BOOKS.

Jacket design by J. Franklin Whitman, Jr.

Printed in the U.S.A.
by
THE TELEGRAPH PRESS
Established in 1831
Harrisburg, Pa.

AUTHOR'S PREFACE

None of the many books on combat intelligence published since the end of World War II have adequately covered the impact of modern warfare. The purpose of this book is to set forth comprehensively the principles and operations of combat intelligence, including a full explanation of the impact of nuclear weapons, helicopters, electronics, and other aspects of modern warfare.

The major concepts covered in this book were developed during the period the author was an instructor at the US Army Command and General Staff College at Fort Leavenworth, Kansas. A great debt of gratitude is owed the many members of the faculty and students who helped in the development and testing of concepts. In particular, I am indebted to Colonel Walter M. Vann, Director of the Department of Staff and Educational Subjects at the US Army Command and General Staff College, during the period 1958-1960. His keen insight and critical analyses helped shape much of the contents of this book.

IRVING HEYMONT
Lieutenant Colonel
Infantry

CONTENTS

CHAPTER 1
WHAT IS INTELLIGENCE?

IMPORTANCE

The decisive factor in warfare has often been combat intelligence. It has been of major influence in every battle, campaign, and war in history, affecting the outcome of struggles between squads and armies. Yet, no other single factor has been so consistently ignored and neglected by unsuccessful commanders. Nothing else has been so universally used and emphasized by successful commanders. Good combat intelligence and its proper use enabled Hannibal to cross the Alps and invade ancient Italy; the lack of it defeated Napoleon at Waterloo and Lee at Gettysburg. It was through the proper use of intelligence of weather and terrain that Von Rundstedt succeeded, at first, in the Battle of the Bulge. General Patton's proper use of counterintelligence enabled him to change the direction of an entire field army and help eliminate the Bulge without disclosing to the Germans serious weakening of the lines in another area. A military commander without an effective combat intelligence system is as handicapped as a blindfolded boxing champion. He may have a powerful punch, but cannot see where to hit or where to protect himself from his opponent's blows.

As important as combat intelligence has been in the past it is even more important now that nuclear weapons are available. The devastating effects of these weapons and the speed, range, and accuracy of their delivery make intelligence the key to battlefield success. The tremendous power of these weapons cannot be brought to bear effectively unless profitable targets are acquired at the appropriate time. A few well-placed nuclear fires, whether of megaton size or of the smaller yield delivered by man-carried Davy Crockett weapons, can bring victory. On the other hand, large numbers of nuclear weapons fired at unprofitable targets may produce only the waste of tremendous resources with no real effect on the outcome of the battle.

1

The denial of information to the enemy is now even more necessary than before to prevent sudden destruction and defeat. Before nuclear firepower became available, commanders with poor combat intelligence could often extricate themselves from unfavorable battlefield entanglements, or make quick changes in their plans without risking annihilation. Now, poor or insufficient intelligence of an enemy with nuclear firepower may well result in complete destruction.

DEFINITION OF INTELLIGENCE

To understand combat intelligence it is necessary first to examine intelligence as it is used by military forces. Intelligence can be broadly defined as *that which is accepted as fact, based on the available information about an actual or potential enemy or area of operations.* A complete definition as given by the US Army is:

"Intelligence is the product resulting from the collection, evaluation, analysis, integration and interpretation of all available information which concerns one or more aspects of foreign nations or of areas of operations which are immediately or potentially significant to planning. Intelligence is developed in peace and war, in contact or out of contact with the enemy."

Intelligence is not the same as *information.* Information is the raw data about an actual or potential enemy or area of operations. As will be explained in detail in chapter 4, intelligence is *derived* from information.

KINDS OF INTELLIGENCE

For the soldier and the statesman there are different kinds of intelligence, depending on the use to which it is put.

NATIONAL INTELLIGENCE. National intelligence is the integrated product of intelligence developed by all government departments which covers the broad aspects of national policy and security. It is of concern to more than one department or agency and ordinarily cannot be produced by a single department or agency. National intelligence is used to coordinate the activities of government departments in developing and executing integrated national policies, plans and programs. The United

States national intelligence organization and activities are explained in appendix I. Military intelligence is the intelligence used in preparing and carrying out *military* policies, plans, and programs. It includes both strategic and *combat intelligence*.

STRATEGIC INTELLIGENCE. Strategic intelligence is used by national planners and high level military commanders (usually field army and above) to plan and carry out peacetime national security measures and wartime military operations. It helps in determining realistic national objectives and is a basis for planning the means of accomplishing these objectives. Strategic intelligence covers the capabilities, vulnerabilities, and probable courses of action of nations. The capabilities of a nation are the actions it can take in war or peace to carry out its national objectives. The capabilities of a nation are determined by analyzing its strengths and weaknesses in comparison with the strengths and weaknesses of another nation or combination of nations. A nation's *vulnerabilities* are those weaknesses which permit action to be taken to reduce that nation's ability or will to fight. Vulnerabilities are determined in the same way as capabilities. Probable courses of action are those things which a nation is *most likely* to do in order to achieve its national objectives.

The components of strategic intelligence are those factors which influence the military capabilities, vulnerabilities, and probable courses of action of nations. The major components are military geography, transportation and telecommunications intelligence, sociological intelligence, political intelligence, economic intelligence, scientific intelligence, armed forces intelligence, and biographical intelligence. None of these factors stands alone. For example, scientific intelligence usually contributes heavily to the production of economic and armed forces intelligence. Finished strategic intelligence is the product of the integration of all of the components.

COMBAT INTELLIGENCE. Combat intelligence is military intelligence which is used in the planning and conduct of tactical and administrative operations. It is the knowledge which the commander requires of the area of operations and the enemy's capabilities and vulnerabilities, in order to evaluate the possible ways in which he can accomplish his mission. Without combat intelligence, no commander can determine the best use of his firepower, the best way in which to maneuver his forces, nor the best means of maintaining the security of his command. In non-combat commands, combat intelligence is required as a basis for decisions on security measures and the best use of the area of operations. In the British Army and the United States Navy, combat intelligence is known as operational intelligence.

Combat intelligence not only warns a commander of the enemy capabilities which can interfere with getting his job done, but also informs him of those enemy vulnerabilities which can be profitably exploited. Taking advantage of an enemy vulnerability often is the factor that assures success.

The difference between strategic and combat intelligence is not clear cut. Both are closely related and have many subjects of common interest. For example, at the start of wartime operations, strategic intelligence such as maps, studies of ports, rivers, towns, and other terrain features, political, sociological, economic, and order of battle studies may be the major source of combat intelligence. Identifications of enemy units and information of characteristics of enemy equipment are used in producing both combat and strategic intelligence. However, combat and strategic intelligence do have some distinctive characteristics. Strategic intelligence is usually produced slowly by assembling and studying a large volume of detailed information and is valid for a considerable period of time. Combat intelligence is usually the product of evaluating and interpreting a lesser amount of information, and usually loses its value very quickly. For example, the capability of a nation to produce field artillery weapons is an item of strategic intelligence that is valid for quite a long time However, the number of enemy field artillery weapons in a certain part of the battlefield is an item of combat intelligence that may lose its validity quickly. In addition to subjects of common interest, combat units assist in the production of strategic intelligence in other ways. Information obtained from prisoners of war on the political and economic conditions within the enemy home land may be important in the production of strategic intelligence, but is of little or no value for combat intelligence.

SPECIALIZED CATEGORIES. There are many other specialized categories of intelligence which contribute to strategic and combat intelligence. These specialized categories usually take their names either from the use to which the intelligence is put or from the type of information on which they are based. The best-known specialized categories are *order of battle intelligence, communications intelligence, electronic intelligence,* and *technical intelligence.* Order of battle intelligence is concerned with enemy units: their strength, identification, disposition, organization, equipment, tactics, combat efficiency and history, and personal data on their key officers. This type of intelligence tells the commander who and what is opposing him. Order of battle intelligence is explained in detail in appendix II. Communications intelligence (*COMINT*) results from studying enemy signal communications. Electronic intelligence (*ELINT*) is the intelligence derived from the study of enemy electromagnetic emissions, except those from nuclear sources. Technical intelligence is concerned with foreign technical developments which have military applications, and with the physical characteristics, performance, capabilities, and limitations of materiel and installations of foreign military forces. It also includes the order of battle of foreign technical intelligence agencies. Technical intelligence is explained in detail in appendix III.

COUNTERINTELLIGENCE. Counterintelligence, while not truly intelligence as defined above, is inseparable from intelligence operations. It covers all activities concerned with destroying the effectiveness of the intelligence activities of a real or potential enemy. Counterintelligence also includes protecting: information from spies, personnel against subversion, and installations and materiel against sabotage. For these reasons, every military intelligence activity has a counterintelligence or security control aspect. Counterintelligence is discussed in detail in chapter 7.

CHAPTER 2

THE PRINCIPLES OF INTELLIGENCE OPERATIONS

BASIC PRINCIPLES ENDURE

Throughout history, weapons and their use have changed but the basic principles of warfare have not. Clubs have been replaced in turn by bows and arrows, spears, muskets, and automatic rifles, but the fundamental principles of war have never lost their validity. In the same manner, nuclear weapons and electronics have not changed the time-proven principles of war but have only modified their application.

Within the past generation, the use of the internal combustion engine in vehicles and airplanes has freed intelligence operations from the limitations imposed by the speed and stamina of the horse. Within recent years, nuclear weapons, radar, and electronic warfare have radically changed intelligence requirements and information collection methods. Techniques and methods will always change to reflect the capabilities of the material which is available at the time. However, like the principles of war, the basic principles of intelligence remain unchanged. An understanding of these principles will make it easier to use new and future methods and equipment and to handle new intelligence requirements.

THE INTELLIGENCE CYCLE

The basic principle of intelligence operations is that all intelligence activities follow a simple cycle based on the commander's mission. The steps in this cycle are:

Collecting information;

Processing the collected information to produce intelligence;

Disseminating and using the intelligence and information;

Planning the collection of information and ordering it done.

This cycle has no definite beginning nor end, and all the steps are carried out at the same time. While new information is being collected, other information is being processed into intelligence.

6

The use of intelligence generates requirements for additional intelligence. Figure 1 shows this four-step intelligence cycle as used in the US Army.

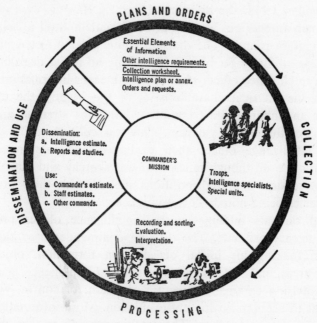

Figure 1. Intelligence cycle.

The US Navy considers the intelligence cycle to have four steps, with collection and its planning combined as one step and dissemination considered as a separate step. The British Army also considers the intelligence cycle to have four steps. They consider the collection and the planning for collection of information to be one step and interpretation as a separate step. Dissemination, according to the British, is not part of the cycle, but necessary for its completion. Regardless of how it may be divided into steps, the intelligence cycle is still the basic process for deciding what must be collected, who will do it, collecting the information, figuring out its meaning, getting the meaning to the users, and its use. The intelligence cycle is applicable to more than just intelligence operations. It is a logical process for any staff officer who must furnish an estimate for the use of a commander in making a decision.

EXAMPLE OF OPERATION OF THE CYCLE. The operation of the intelligence cycle can be illustrated by one of the actions of the 7th US Infantry Division during World War II. In December 1943, the division—based on Hawaii—was ordered to make an amphibious attack on the Kwajalein Atoll to seize and defend certain islands. The division commander directed his staff to prepare estimates for his use in making an initial decision. The division intelligence officer obtained the meager information available on the physical characteristics of the islands, the existing weather and hydrographic conditions, and the strength and dispositions of the enemy garrison. This was *collection.*

The intelligence officer then evaluated and interpreted this information, even though much of it was sketchy and out of date. Maps were drawn and dispositions plotted with their probably inaccuracies being noted. This was *processing.*

Based on this intelligence, the intelligence officer prepared an intelligence estimate. The division commander used this estimate in making his initial decision on formation, objectives, landing areas, and so forth. This was *use* of intelligence.

The division commander's initial decision, of course, was not sufficient to accomplish the entire mission. More information was needed for later decisions. The intelligence officer was directed to obtain answers to certain essential elements of information. For example, the division commander was particularly concerned about the characteristics of a certain reef. The intelligence officer made plans for collecting the information necessary to answer this essential element of information and others. His plans were based on careful analysis of the essential elements of information in terms of *indications* which would give the necessary answers, and on the capabilities of the available collection agencies. Historically, the intelligence officer directed a regimental combat team to make a night reconnaissance to determine whether landing craft could cross that reef at all the tide stages. This was *planning the collection effort.*

Early on D-Day, the division reconnaissance troop captured an enemy tug. The hydrographic charts found on the tug gave the needed information and similar information for the whole area. This was *collection* again.

The intelligence officer promptly evaluated the information. It had been collected by reliable agencies and was apparently a true picture of hydrographic conditions. Navy personnel helped interpret the information as regards conditions across the reef in question. This was *processing* again.

The resulting intelligence contributed to the growing picture of the area. The division commander used this intelligence in planning the further operations necessary to complete the mission. In addition, it was used by subordinate commanders in making their plans. This was *use* again.

This example is based only on one single item. At the same time, the collection of information on other items was being directed, the information collected, processed, and used.

INTELLIGENCE MUST BE USEFUL

The second basic principle is that intelligence must be useful. Intelligence produced merely for the sake of increasing knowledge is only interesting. Useful intelligence adds knowledge and understanding of the particular problem being considered so that decisions may be reached. It must also be adequate for the use to which it is to be put. By thoroughly understanding the nature of the problem or the commander's mission, it is possible to determine what intelligence will be useful. Lack of this thorough understanding often results in wasted effort and in the production of intelligence which is of no use to the commander.

INTELLIGENCE MUST BE TIMELY

The principle of usefulness leads to the third basic principle: timeliness. The best intelligence is worthless if it does not reach the user in time. Conditions in combat, particularly enemy dispositions and weather, are continually changing. Frequently, decisions are based on incomplete intelligence because the situation requires the decision before complete intelligence can be produced. The competing requirements for timeliness on one hand and accuracy and completeness on the other hand will often require careful judgment. An understanding of the intended use of the intelligence and the problem for which it is required helps in judging the amount of accuracy and completeness that may be sacrificed. One of the reasons for General Lee's successful retreat after being defeated at Gettysburg, was General Meade's insistence on complete intelligence of the enemy before starting to pursue. On the nuclear battlefield, characterized by fast moving, widely dispersed forces and fluid operations, it can be expected that decisions, more than ever in the past, will be based on incomplete intelligence.

Because use of nuclear weapons can radically change the balance of combat power in moments, timeliness is particularly urgent in intelligence on potential nuclear targets. In producing such intelligence, timeliness is necessary at every stage of the intelligence cycle. This is brought out in figure 2.

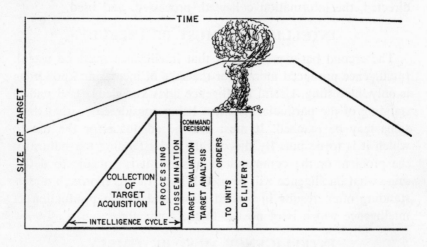

◄—Delivery in this period is less than ideal ——►◄—Ideal delivery time —►◄—Past ideal delivery time —►

Figure 2. Build-up and decline of a target.

The figure shows schematically the time for build-up and decline of a target in comparison to the *ideal* time for acquiring the target, processing the information (recording, evaluation, and interpretation), disseminating the intelligence and information, and acting on the intelligence. In this *ideal* situation, each phase of the intelligence cycle has been accomplished in time to deliver the fires before the target has declined in size to the point where the fires would be unprofitable. In the target acquisition or collection phase, there was no appreciable time lag between the target build-up and the availability of the information. Processing was timely.

Actually, evaluation and interpretation, to be timely, is frequently made on the basis of incomplete information. The speed of warfare does not always allow time for collecting additional and confirming information. Frequently, target attacks will have to be based on incomplete intelligence and information. By the time complete information of the target is obtained, the target may have dissipated. In the future, automatic data processing system will help in rapidly making available all known pertinent information.

INTELLIGENCE IS AN INTEGRAL PART OF OPERATIONS

Another basic principle is that intelligence operations *are not isolated* operations. Intelligence operations are an integral part of the operations of *all* units, both combat and service. The over-all operations of any armed force in combat is measured and greatly affected by the intelligence which it develops and uses. Tactics and strategy of armies, fleets, air forces, and even very small units, are at the same time the cause and effect of intelligence operations. To assume that intelligence operations are of concern only to intelligence specialists is a guarantee of eventual defeat, if not early disaster. Staff officers issuing operational orders and those responsible for intelligence operations must work as one team. Only in this way can orders and plans take full advantage of all that is known of the situation and of the enemy capabilities and weaknesses. Both intelligence and operational personnel are jointly responsible for this close coordination. Any differences of opinion on the meaning of the available intelligence must be decided by the commander. If this is not done promptly, it may result in a unit being given inconsistent orders.

COMMANDER'S NEEDS

Intelligence must fit the needs of the commander. This is an extension of the basic principle of *use*. All commanders do not need the same intelligence. This principle is best illustrated by briefly discussing the needs of different commanders of intelligence of different geographical areas. Intelligence plans and operations are concerned with definite areas, particularly the *area of influence* of the command. Of course, there are some overlapping areas between different commands. The area of influence is that part of a commander's area in which, by his own means, he is capable of directly influencing operations by the use of his combat power. Intelligence operations, however, include the *area of interest* of the command to the extent that they permit planning for the forward movement of the area of influence. The area of interest surrounds the area of influence and is the area in which supporting and adjacent forces conduct operations. Figure 3 shows the relation between the area of interest and the area of influence.

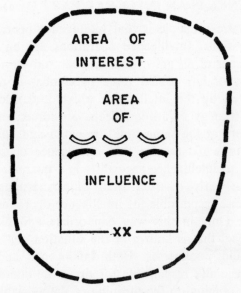

Figure 3. Comparison of area of influence and area of interest.

For Army forces, the area of interest contains those enemy ground forces which could interfere with the accomplishment of the commander's mission if they were employed in time in his area of influence. An understanding of the areas of interest and influence of a command permits the guiding of intelligence operations and the assignment of means of collecting information. Producing intelligence of the area of influence usually takes highest priority, and a unit should have under its control all the means that it can economically support for producing intelligence of this area. Normally, most of the intelligence of the area of interest of a unit is furnished by higher headquarters.

The area of influence of a command normally extends to the maximum effective range of the firepower available to the command.

For US Army units, the approximate depths of the area of influence are:

Battle Group (Combat Command) .... 5-15 miles
Division .... 15-50 miles
Corps .... 50-75 miles
Army .... 75-300 miles

PLANNING

Intelligence operations require planning. Planning permits filling intelligence needs in time, arranging for means to fulfill requirements, and properly supervising the production of the intelligence. By proper planning it is possible to keep up with changing conditions by developing and quickly taking advantage of new information sources and improving methods of producing and disseminating intelligence. This kind of planning results in the collection of information having future value as well as that which is needed for current projects. Had there been proper intelligence planning, the United States Army would not have found itself without adequate maps of Cuba and Puerto Rico when the war with Spain broke out in 1898.

FLEXIBILITY

Intelligence operations must be flexible. While standard procedures generally make for more effective intelligence operations, established procedures are not followed blindly. Procedures must change to meet the requirements resulting from unexpected situations. If this is not done, a failure in intelligence operations may result. Intelligence operations are based on reason and judgment and are not shackled by fixed procedures.

IMAGINATION AND RESOURCEFULNESS

The principle of flexibility leads to the principle of imagination and resourcefulness. Imagination and foresight are essential for the production of good intelligence. Policies and procedures which limit imagination or initiative in intelligence operations are avoided like a plague. Everyone connected with intelligence operations—and that includes everyone in the military service—must use resourcefulness if useful intelligence is to be produced and gotten to the user in time. How are imagination and resourcefulness used? Above all, the self-evident is never accepted without great caution. Military forces carry out deception to cause the enemy to make false assumptions. Regardless of appearances the possibility of enemy deception is always considered. The Trojan Horse of ancient history illustrates the disastrous results of accepting the self-evident without caution. It must also always be assumed in intelligence operations that the situation always changes. When the enemy is apparently not doing anything, it is necessary to redouble efforts to find signs of changes in the situation or confirmation that nothing significant has really changed. If there is any doubt that the enemy will adopt a particular capability, it must be assumed that the enemy will adopt the capability that causes the greatest damage to his opponent. To assume that the enemy will do nothing to change the current situation may be dangerous. The Germans were helped in achieving surprise in their Ardennes offensive of December 1944—the Battle of the Bulge— because too many intelligence officers assumed that the Germans would continue the defense they had maintained for months.

SECURITY

As pointed out in the first chapter, all intelligence operations have security aspects. This leads to the principle of security in intelligence operations. Security measures are always required to keep the enemy from getting information about intelligence operations and the intelligence produced. The enemy has an advantage if he knows how much his opponent knows of his capabilities, vulnerabilities, and probable courses of action. The enemy also has an advantage if he can learn the extent of his success in deception measures. There were no changes in the original plan for the battle of El Alamein because Field Marshal Montgomery knew that his deception measures on the south flank had succeeded in deceiving Rommel. The effect of loss to the enemy of whole intelligence estimates and similar items is obvious. Yet the total effects of compromise of small pieces of information and intelligence are equally dangerous. Every military force collects these small pieces in order to build a complete intelligence picture. This is the usual manner in which intelligence is developed. Only in fiction does anyone make off with whole campaign plans. However, it is necessary to understand that there is a big difference between security and secrecy. Intelligence is useless unless it gets to the persons who need it and security measures must not prevent intelligence getting to them. Further, security measures must not prevent disseminating intelligence among those involved in intelligence operations and the ready exchange of information. Unless there is such a free exchange, the production of the best possible intelligence is slowed and handicapped.

ATTACK ON PEARL HARBOR. One of the most spectacular failures in intelligence operations and the use of intelligence resulted in the successful Japanese attack on Pearl Harbor on December 7, 1941. This attack was thoroughly investigated by the Congressional Joint Committee on the investigation of the Pearl Harbor Attack. After a detailed investigation, the committee developed a number of principles, the violation of which had made possible the Japanese success. The principles developed by the Committee that are applicable to intelligence operations are about the same as the ones described earlier. The applicable principles developed by the committee are repeated below exactly:

> Operational and intelligence work requires centralization of authority and clear cut allocation of responsibility. Any doubt as to whether outposts should be given information should always be resolved in favor of supplying the information.
>
> Complacency and procrastination are out of place when sudden and decisive action is of the essence.
>
> The coordination and proper evaluation of intelligence in time of stress must be ensured by continuity of service and centralization of responsibility in competent officials.
>
> There is no substitute for imagination and resourcefulness on the part of supervisory and intelligence officials.
>
> Communications must be characterized by clarity, forthrightness, and appropriateness.
>
> Procedures must be sufficiently flexible to meet the exigencies of unusual situations.

Restriction of highly confidential information to a minimum number of officials, while often necessary, should not be carried to the point of prejudicing work of the organization.

There is great danger of being blinded by the self-evident. Officials should at all times give subordinates the benefit of significant information.

Failure can be avoided in the long run only by preparation for any eventuality.

SUMMARY

In summary, the principles of intelligence are:

Intelligence activities follow a simple cycle based on the commander's mission;

Intelligence must be useful, timely, and fit the needs of the commander;

Intelligence operations are not isolated operations;

Intelligence operations must be flexible, require imagination, foresight, and the protection of security operations.

With these principles in mind, we can proceed to examine the activities in each step of the intelligence cycle.

CHAPTER 3

COLLECTION OF INFORMATION

Since information of the enemy and the area of operations is the raw material from which intelligence is produced, collection of information will be discussed first.

COLLECTION SOURCES

To understand the collection of information and its processing into intelligence, it is important to know the difference between sources and agencies. Sources of information are simply the actual origin from which information is obtained. The major source of information for production of combat intelligence is enemy activity. Other common sources include prisoners of war; civilians in the area; recovered military personnel; captured enemy documents and materiel; enemy signal communications and other electromagnetic emissions; duds; shell and missile fragments; craters and contaminated areas; nuclear bursts; maps and photographs; weather forecasts; and studies and reports.

The volume and type of information of enemy activities that can be collected are limited by the ability of the enemy to keep his activities from being detected and by the effectiveness of the means used to collect information. A typical measure to keep activities from being detected is the use of artillery fire to prevent the distinctive noise of tank movements from being heard. The inability of radar to observe except on line of sight is an example of a limitation in collecting information of enemy activities.

Information that the enemy is NOT performing certain activities is often more valuable than information of what he is doing or has done. The fact that enemy has not moved his reserves may influence a commander's decision.

Other sources of information are discussed in appendix IV.

COLLECTION AGENCIES

An agency is any individual or unit which collects or proc-

17

esses information—or does both. Collection agencies obtain information by many different means. The more common of these are interrogation, examination, observation and listening posts, use of ground and airborne surveillance devices, air and ground reconnaissance, radiological monitoring and survey, and interception of enemy electromagnetic radiation. Imagination and in-

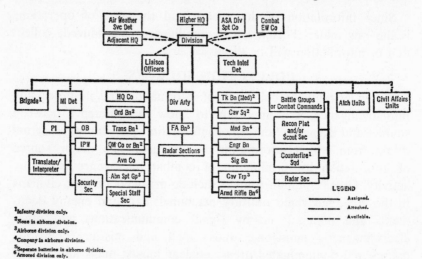

Figure 4. Division collection agencies.

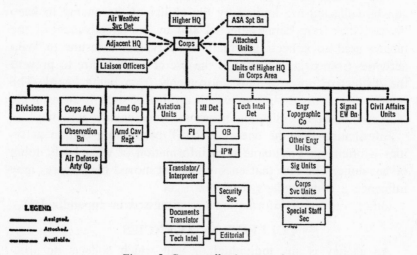

Figure 5. Corps collection agencies.

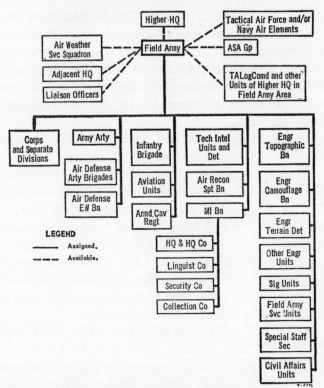

Figure 6. Field army collection agencies.

genuity are used by collection agencies to develop and improve methods of collecting information.

There are many different kinds of collection agencies. At each headquarters the subordinate, adjacent, and higher commands are considered as collection agencies. Agencies of this kind available to various headquarters within the field army are shown in figures 4, 5 and 6.

Some collection agencies, such as armored cavalry units, are specifically organized to collect information by combat operations. Others, such as Army aviation or Air Force reconnaissance units, are organized specifically to collect information by aerial observation. Aviation collection agencies can collect rapidly information on enemy dispositions, the location and nature of enemy activities, installations, terrain features, nuclear bursts, damage estimates, and the extent and degree of radiological contaminations.

TECHNICAL INTELLIGENCE DETACHMENTS. These are collection agencies consisting of specially trained personnel of the technical services. The information they collect and provide includes the use and capabilities of enemy equipment. Within the army, technical intelligence detachments are assigned to corps and higher headquarters. Appendix III discusses the operations of these detachments.

MILITARY INTELLIGENCE SPECIALISTS. These include prisoner of war interrogators, interpreters, security unit personnel, imagery interpreters, and strategic research and analysis personnel. Appendix V describes the organization and functions of the military intelligence specialists and units within a field army.

ELECTRONIC WARFARE UNITS. Such units are now required because of the widespread use of electronic equipment by modern armies. These units collect information on enemy capabilities to conduct electronic warfare. Supporting electronic warfare units must be kept informed of pertinent information requirements if they are to produce useful information.

US ARMY SECURITY AGENCY UNITS AND SIMILAR UNITS OF THE AIR FORCE AND NAVY. These collect information from enemy electromagnetic emissions. They can also procure information from similar higher and adjacent units. Army divisions, corps, field armies are usually supported by US Army Security Agency units.

STAY-BEHIND UNITS. Combat elements isolated in the enemy rear, either deliberately or as a result of the tide of battle, may be very useful, especially for target acquisition. Deliberate stay-behind units require special training and equipment, particularly in communications. As part of the normal training program, all units should be trained in stay-behind roles in the event of isolation in the enemy rear area.

SPIES, ARMY SPECIAL FORCES, AND GUERRILLAS. These are particularly effective on the nuclear battlefield where units are widely dispersed. Operating deep in the enemy rear area, they can collect information that is also particularly valuable for target acquisition. These agencies must have suitable communications to permit timely receipt of orders and reporting of information.

The use of stay-behind units, spies, Army Special Forces units, and guerrillas for collecting information is influenced by their ability to move and communicate. Their ability to move is limited by the constant threat of detection and by supply problems. Constant communication with friendly forces is impossible because of the possibility of disclosing their presence and the location of their communications equipment. Special arrangements are required for reporting urgent information and orders. In using these agencies for collecting information consideration must be given to the time required to get orders to them and information back. The activities of these agencies must be closely coordinated with the friendly use of long range weapons in order to prevent their destruction.

TECHNICAL SERVICES. Special staff officers and the troops under their control or command are often neglected and frequently misunderstood in their roles as collection agencies. The following special staff officers can furnish information of the types indicated.

Chemical. Enemy chemical and biological warfare troops, materiel, installations, tactical, and capabilities. The location, size, duration, and effects of chemical and biological contamination. The location, extent, and degree of radiological contamination caused by or expected from nuclear bursts.

Engineer. Terrain, enemy fortifications, engineer troops, tactics, materiel, and capabilities. Terrain information includes trafficability studies, and data on streams, landing beaches, ports, railroads, canals, pipelines, airfields, and bridges. Special engineer units prepare terrain studies, topographic maps, terrain models, and map supplements.

Medical. Medical and public health aspects of the area including health hazards due to weather or disease. Capabilities and limitations of enemy medical materiel and methods and information and documents from prisoners under medical care.

Ordnance. Capabilities, limitations, and vulnerabilities of enemy ordnance materiel; maintenance methods and weaknesses; and location of enemy ammunition stocks.

Quartermaster. Location and size of enemy petroleum and

general supplies stocks. Capabilities, limitations, and adequacy of enemy quartermaster materiel and services.

Signal. Capabilities, limitations, and vulnerabilities of enemy signal equipment and personnel. Practices, capabilities, limitations, and vulnerabilities of enemy signal and electronic warfare operations. Use of radar and other sensory devices and ability of enemy to maintain communications.

Transportation. Characteristics, capacity, and adequacy of enemy transportation. Military use of transportation routes and equipment in the area of operations, to include railroads, highways, waterways, ports, and beaches with particular reference to capabilities to move units and supplies.

RECONNAISSANCE

A major method for obtaining information for combat intelligence purposes throughout the history of warfare has been reconnaissance. The same is true in modern warfare. Reconnaissance in its many forms provides a large portion of the intelligence picture for units in contact. Generally, reconnaissance is a mission undertaken to obtain, through observation, information about the activities of an enemy and the physical characteristics of a particular area. While this observation includes the use of sensory devices such as cameras and radar, it does not include espionage.

Counterreconnaissance operations are those measures and activities used to prevent or reduce the effectiveness of enemy observation of friendly forces and their areas of operation. Counterreconnaissance and counterintelligence measures are closely tied together. Effective counterreconnaissance activities become more difficult with the increased dispersion of units in modern warfare. Effective counterreconnaissance is of great importance in achieving surprise and in preventing the enemy from learning of targets in the forward battle areas.

Ground reconnaissance is the best known method of gaining tactical information. Ground reconnaissance is performed by personnel manning observation posts and/or surveillance devices, elements of all arms, and units especially designed to perform ground reconnaissance. Of Army troops which perform ground reconnaissance, infantry, armor, and engineer elements are best suited for patrolling. Armored cavalry reconnaissance units are excellent for reconnaissance missions deep in enemy areas. The depth at which patrols may operate is increased by using helicopters to deliver and retrieve patrols. The ability of patrols to provide timely information depends on their mobility and communications for sending back information and receiving new instructions.

RECONNAISSANCE PRINCIPLES. The broad principles of reconnaissance patrolling that apply to the Army, Navy, and Air Force are:

Make and keep contact with the enemy as soon as possible. By working continuously to the front, flank, and to the rear of the enemy and keeping him under constant observation, the location, identification, disposition, and strength of the enemy are determined and the approach of enemy reinforcements detected. In doing this, ground patrols and reconnaissance units are assisted where possible by light aircraft.

Maneuver freely. Patrols and reconnaissance units must keep pace with the enemy and base their actions on those of the enemy and not on those of the friendly forces. To obtain the greatest amount of information, reconnaissance units and patrols do not restrict themselves to roads, valleys, and ridge lines or other well defined routes. Go where the enemy goes.

Fight only to gain information. Reconnaissance of the enemy is most effective when it is not detected. Reconnaissance elements fight only to prevent destruction or capture, to take prisoners, or when the desired information can be obtained only by combat.

Report everything, including negative information. Often, information that is important does not seem to be so at the time it is collected. All information is reported as soon as possible. Negative information is important because it shows where the enemy is not, or where he is not going at a particular time.

RECONNAISSANCE IN FORCE. A special type of reconnaissance is a reconnaissance in force. This is a limited objective operation by a considerable force to uncover and test the enemy's dispositions and strengths, or to develop other intelligence information. A reconnaissance in force is usually planned and executed as a limited objective attack. The Allied raid on Dieppe, France, in August 1942 is an example of a large scale reconnaissance in force. The information on German beach defenses secured as a result of the raid helped in the planning of the Normandy invasion of 1944.

If the enemy situation must be developed along a broad front, a reconnaissance in force may be conducted using strong probing actions to determine the enemy situation at selected points. The force must be strong enough to cause the enemy to react and thereby disclose his location, dispositions, and strength. Because a reconnaissance in force is used where the character of the opposition is unknown, a balanced force is employed.

Even when used to gather information, the commander of a reconnaissance force is alert to seize any opportunity to take advantage of tactical success. The United Nations counteroffensive in January, 1951, in Korea was a result of exploiting the success achieved by a reconnaissance in force. At first, the US I and IX Corps advanced on a broad front with one division each in multiple columns. When these divisions met with little opposition, the UN commander, General Ridgway, promptly committed additional forces and changed the operation from a reconnaissance in force to a full-scale attack.

Care should be taken before undertaking a reconnaissance in force. The operation may result in unacceptable losses, disclose the commander's intentions, or may cause an unwanted large-scale battle. When the enemy has tactical nuclear weapons, the risk in presenting a profitable target may outweigh the value of the information which can be obtained.

RECONNAISSANCE BY FIRE. Another method of reconnaissance is reconnaissance by fire. By this method fire is placed on a suspected enemy position either to destroy camouflage or to cause the enemy to react through movement or return of fire. Enemy reaction may permit observation of his location, dispositions, and strength. This type of reconnaissance was used extensively toward the end of the Korean war when both sides had well developed dug-in defenses with many alternate positions. Reconnaissance by fire frequently disclosed the occupied positions.

COUNTERRECONNAISSANCE. Counterreconnaissance opperations are based, on the other hand, on the actions of the friendly forces being screened. Counterreconnaissance elements destroy or neutralize enemy reconnaissance elements. Screening forces are placed in depth for mutual support and to limit penetrations by enemy reconnaissance elements. Counterreconnaissance screens may be established behind natural obstacles which limit avenues of approach or restrict the enemy reconnaissance effort to certain areas. It may meet the enemy reconnaissance elements and destroy them by offensive combat. A counterreconnaissance screen may be either moving or stationary, depending upon the activities of the force being screened.

AIR RECONNAISSANCE. Air reconnaissance, using any type of manned or drone aircraft, includes not only visual, photographic, and weather observation but also observation by airborne radar, infrared, electronic, and other sensory devices. It is an effective and generally reliable means for penetrating deep into enemy territory and of securing rapidly information of terrain and enemy activities over large areas. Air reconnaissance is frequently used in conjunction with ground reconnaissance forces and in locating enemy forces which may slow or destroy them. It is also used for confirming and obtaining additional information of activities and installations detected in other ways. Air reconnaissance is limited by bad weather conditions and effective enemy air defense measures. Appendix VI covers aerial reconnaissance request procedures.

With the widespread use of electronics by modern armies, *electronic air reconnaissance* is used to locate electromagnetic radiation devices operated by the enemy. The information obtained may be used to determine the enemy's electronic order of battle, for planning effective electronic countermeasures, locating areas which will require additional reconnaissance and finally, for determining targets for attack. Typical objectives of electronic air reconnaissance include radar (gun-laying, early warning, and Ground Control Intercept (*GCI*)), navigation systems for missiles and drones, communications systems, and electronic countermeasure facilities. Electronic air reconnaissance missions are requested in the same manner as other forms of aerial reconnaissance.

Visual air reconnaissance is the gathering of information by visual observation from aircraft. Timely information of enemy activities can be obtained rapidly by this means. The use of voice recording and camera equipment increases the accuracy and detail of visual observation reports. Visual reconnaissance is excellent for fast reporting of fleeting targets to units capable of attacking them. As with all forms of aerial reconnaissance, visual air reconnaissance is limited by bad weather, camouflage, and enemy countermeasures. Moreover, there are limitations on the keenness of sight of pilots and observers. In addition, locations based on visual air observation are often inaccurate because of the observer's difficulty in keeping himself correctly oriented. Visual reconnaissance missions are usually area search, specific search, route reconnaissance and artillery adjustment. Each type of mission has a different purpose and requires different actions by the pilot and observer.

Area search, or observation of an area, is conducted at specific intervals for a specific period of time. It is most effective for sparsely populated or open areas. Because this type of reconnaissance is mainly concerned with general information and not specific targets, a large area may be searched, up to 2,500 square miles. When more detailed information is required, the area covered is reduced.

Specific search is used to observe closely one or a few points for specific information. It is best employed over wooded or rough terrain and over heavily populated areas and to supplement area search missions. Normally, it is not flown on a regular schedule as is area search.

Route reconnaissance is observation along lines of communications such as roads, railroads, and waterways to determine enemy activity or the conditions of the route. It is carried out on a point-to-point or town-to-town basis over main transportation routes and may pass through several search areas. Route reconnaissance is also used to supplement area search.

Artillery adjustment may be used to adjust fire of long range artillery and naval gunfire, as well as the fire of infantry weapons. The Army usually uses its own aircraft for this type of mission.

Aerial photography is one of the best means of collecting information of terrain and the enemy. It is the fastest means of obtaining detailed terrain information of large areas. Aerial photographs of the same area taken at different times (called "repetitive cover") when properly studied, permit detailed analysis of enemy activity. Good photointerpretation, including comparative study, produces large quantities of accurate, detailed information. Air photos overcome many of the limitations of visual reconnaissance. The photo interpreter can detect enemy camouflage better than the visual observer. A disadvantage of aerial photographic reconnaissance is that time is needed for

	Major Uses	Types of Photos	Area of Coverage	Frequency	Distribution
Basic Cover.	General intelligence requirements, such as basic information on terrain, routes of communication, and enemy activities. Planning operations. Mapping.	Usually vertical stereo pairs.	Projected areas of operations.	As necessary to show seasonal changes.	Normally requested by field army which makes automatic distribution to subordinate units according to areas of interest. Supplementary issues are made as necessary.
Tactical Cover.	Conduct of current tactical operations. Target acquisition.	Usually vertical stereo pairs.	Unit areas of influence and specified portions of the unit area of interest.	As required by the tactical situation, terrain characteristics, and other variables. At times, daily coverage of only portions of the battle area is required. In moving situations, only coverage of specified areas and immediate objectives may be required.	Normally requested by by division and higher headquarters.
Special Cover.	Study of specific targets or objectives for information for immediate requirements and for specific planning.	As required.	As required.	As required.	As required.
Mapping Cover.	Preparation and revision of maps.	Usually small scale vertical stereo pairs.[1]	As required.	As required.	Normally requested by corps and higher headquarters and distributed to topographic units.

[1]Often supplemented with large scale photos of culturally developed areas.

Figure 7. Types of aerial photographic coverage.

processing film, interpreting the prints and disseminating the information. The usual types of aerial photographic coverage are shown in figure 7.

A unit requesting aerial photography indicates the desired approximate scale, type, and specific information required. G2 Air personnel determine the exact scale needed to satisfy the requirement. Figure 8 shows the minimum scales for identifying and interpreting various targets. Changes in atmospheric conditions and film processing may require alteration of these scales.

The unit requesting photo reconnaissance is not responsible for flight planning or flight lines. At times it may be necessary for the G2 Air to do flight planning or specify flight lines. However, better coverage is usually secured by giving the aviation unit the greatest freedom in these matters. Because intelligence

Subject	Minimum scale for detail interpretation	Minimum scale for identification
Aircraft	1:5,000	1:10,000
Airfields	1:12,000	1:30,000
Barbed wire	1:5,000	1:10,000
Beaches	1:10,000	
Communications	1:5,000	1:15,000
Directional finders	1:5,000	1:15,000
Dumps	1:10,000	1:30,000
Field artillery	1:5,000	1:15,000
Heavy air defense	1:5,000	1:20,000
Light air defense	1:5,000	1:10,000
Pillboxes	1:5,000	1:10,000
Railway cars	1:10,000	1:20,000
Roads	1:5,000	
Searchlights	1:5,000	1:15,000
Strong points	1:5,000	1:10,000
Surface-to-air missiles	1:5,000	1:10,000
Surface-to-surface missiles	1:5,000	1:10,000
Trenches	1:10,000	1:15,000
Under water and beach obstacles	1:2,000	1:10,000
Urban areas	1:15,000	1:60,000
Vegetation		1:20,000
Vehicles	1:5,000	1:10,000
Vessels	1:5,000	1:10,000

Figure 8. Reference scale for photointerpretation.

requirements frequently permit considerable latitude in size, shape, and scale of the photos, additional or better coverage can often be provided with the same effort by not overly prescribing the manner in which the mission is to be performed.

Night air reconnaissance, although used for the same purposes as day air reconnaissance, usually requires navigation aids and artificial illumination for photography. Information of enemy activity usually unobtainable at any other time may be gotten by night air reconnaisance.

Weather reconnaissance by air, ground, or sea, obtains data on areas for use in preparing weather analysis and forecasts. *Scheduled* weather reconnaissance missions make weather observations (to include atmospheric soundings) at predetermined locations and at scheduled times. *Unscheduled* weather reconnaissance missions investigate, as required, weather conditions which will affect observations. Air weather reconnaissance missions are used to obtain special weather reports of conditions along the routes and in the vicinity of objective areas for ground operations and for operations dependent on the use of aircraft. Having timely weather reports permits immediate decisions such as diversion, change of flight track, and cancellation or changes of missions.

The activities detected by airborne *radar* and *infrared* devices may be indicated by a scope presentation for instantaneous viewing, photographic recording for detailed study and re-use, and transmission to a ground station. Airborne radar and infrared sensory devices are particularly valuable during periods of poor visibility.

Airborne radar, in drones or manned aircraft, is valuable as a moving target indicator. Radar information of movements must be supplemented by other means, such as visual observation and photography in order to better identify the activity detected by the radar. Airborne radars can cover large areas quickly. Side-looking airborne radars can operate from behind the forward edge of the friendly dispositions. Airborne radar is dependent upon line of sight and the use of ground based tracking and plotting systems to locate the detected activities. Radar devices can be made ineffective by enemy electronic countermeasures.

Airborne passive *infrared* and *thermal* detection devices are valuable in penetrating camouflage and collecting information at night. As with airborne radar, the information obtained by these devices must be checked by other means, such as visual observation and photography which can better identify the detected activity. Airborne passive infrared and thermal detection devices, like airborne radars, can cover large areas quickly but are limited to line of sight coverage and the use of ground based tracking and plotting systems to locate the detected activities. Passive infrared and thermal detection devices cannot be jammed by countermeasures but they also cannot readily differentiate between real activities and enemy deception measures. The efficiency of these devices is reduced by fog, clouds, and precipitation. The interpretation of the raw data produced by infrared and thermal detection devices requires highly skilled interpreters.

Army *observation aircraft* can perform day and night visual, electronic, photo, radar, infrared, and radiological survey missions. Aerial reconnaissance missions performed by Army aircraft usually result in information getting to the requesting unit faster than if the mission is flown by either the Air Force or Navy. The radio communications in Army aircraft permit direct transmission of information to battle group, combat command, and higher headquarters and in-flight diversion to higher priority missions. However, the effectiveness of Army aircraft for aerial reconnaissance is limited by the shallow depth over the enemy area to which they can penetrate. This is a result of the low performance characteristics of Army aircraft which make them particularly vulnerable to enemy air defense measures, particularly during daylight.

Tactical reconnaissance wings of a *tactical air force (TAF)* of the Air Force normally support Army operations. These wings include both reconnaissance-fighter and reconnaissance-bomber aircraft. Information on significant sightings made in flight is immediately transmitted over the *TAF* tactical air observation net which is monitored by the spot report receivers at Army units and the Air Force Sector Control Centers *(SCC)*. TAF high performance reconnaissance aircraft, with fighter cover when required, are used to reconnoiter over the forward areas as well as deep over the enemy area.

Naval and Marine aircraft may provide reconnaissance support for Army units. In amphibious operations involving Army units, Navy and Marine carrier-based aircraft furnish air reconnaissance support and the Navy/Marine Corps system for requesting and coordinating Air reconnaissance is used. In other types of operations, Navy and Marine air reconnaissance support may be used when aircraft carriers are within range. In these situations, Navy and Marine air reconnaissance activities are coordinated by the Tactical Air Force and normal Army-Air Force request and coordinating procedures are used. In exceptional cases, Navy and Marine air units may provide direct support to the Army units in non-amphibious operations. In such situations special procedures for requesting and coordinating air reconnaissance may be established. Because of limited photo reproduction facilities aboard aircraft carriers, Army air photo reproduction units may be stationed with naval air reconnaissance units. Air photos are then delivered to Army units by either Navy or Marine or Army couriers. Army photo interpreters and liaison officers are normally located with Navy or Marine air reconnaissance units when they are in support of the Army.

COORDINATING AND PLANNING. The intelligence officer plans and coordinates reconnaissance activities, except for reconnaissance in force operations. He consults with the operations officer on the availability of troops and with the rest of the staff to ensure that reconnaissance actvities are coordinated with other operations. Reconnaissance activities of subordinate units are coordinated to avoid undesirable duplication of effort and conflicts between friendly elements. Generally, night reconnaissance requires most coordination and control.

Reconnaissance plans must be completed early enough to allow the executing units adequate time to make their own preparations, conduct the reconnaissance, and report the results by the time specified. Adjacent and supporting units concerned are informed of reconnaissance plans to ensure coordination. When appropriate, plans are made for interrogating participating personnel after the reconnaissance has been completed.

In assigning reconnaissance missions, broad generalizations such as "report strength and dispositions of the enemy" are avoided. The specific time that the information is desired or the latest time that it will be of value is included in the order or request. When more than one mission is assigned to one agency, definite priorities should be assigned in accordance with the importance of the information requested and the time it is needed.

COMBAT SURVEILLANCE

Another major method for the collection of information is combat surveillance. It is defined as the continuous, all-weather, day and night systematic watch over the battle area to provide timely information for ground tactical operations. It consists of the systematic *observation* of air, surface, or subsurface areas by visual, listening, electronic, photographic or other sensory devices. The principal electronic devices used in combat surveillance are radar and infrared instruments. Combat surveillance also helps in the control of friendly forces by assisting in determining the locations of friendly combat elements.

The use of combat surveillance is as old as warfare. However, the use of radar and infrared devices is new. Combat surveillance combines the use of all means of observation, old and new. No one means of surveillance, technical or nontechnical, is complete in itself. All methods and devices are used to provide the pieces of information required to make a composite picture, primarily of the commander's area of influence. The soldier is a major collector of information in combat surveillance. His capabilities are improved by optical instruments, battlefield illumination equipment, and other short-range surveillance devices that permit observation of close-in areas to detect troops and materiel as well as movement during periods of poor visibility. Surveillance methods and devices such as photointerpretation, radar, infrared devices, reconnaissance patrols, and forward observers provide a part of the collection effort and record of target information. In support are personnel and units which can extract and interpret the informa-

Figure 9. Pilots being debriefed.

Figure 10. Radiac instrument in use.

tion, describe the enemy situation, and define the location, composition, and disposition of a hostile target. Combat surveillance equipment and its use are discussed in appendix VII.

RADIATION FALLOUT

Battlefield use of nuclear weapons results in a requirement for information that never existed before—information of radiological contamination. This contamination is caused by the radioactive particles produced by nuclear explosions settling on the earth. Because of the large area that radioactive fallout can cover, and the relatively long time that normal use of that area may not be possible, fallout can be a key factor in determining the practicality of a given course of action. The intelligence officer is responsible for the supervision of the collection of information on fallout because, like rain, it affects the use of the area of operations.

In estimating the influence of fallout on any operation, the commander and his staff must know the location, size, shape, and intensity of the fallout area. The direction and size of this area depends on the direction, velocity, and types of winds from ground level to the top of the cloud caused by the nuclear explosion. Within the Army, raw weather data is obtained from Air Weather Service detachments of the Air Force located at corps, field army, and in the communications zone, and from the meteorological sections of artillery units. The prediction of the size and shape of the area that will be covered by fallout is based on the weather data, the actual or assumed ground zero and yield of the nuclear burst, and the time and height of the burst. After the nuclear explosion, the prediction is modified to reflect the reported ground zero, yield, and height of burst. When an enemy detonation occurs, all units with the capability of determining the ground zero, yield, and height of burst report this information to the next higher headquarters as rapidly as possible.

MONITORING FALLOUT. Monitoring is the determination of the *presence* and *intensity* of radioactivity actually on the ground by using radiac instruments to detect and measure radiation.

There is no special organization for monitoring within the US Army; it is a unit responsibility. Monitoring makes possible prompt warning of the presence of radioactive contamination. The frequency of monitoring is usually specified as an item of standing operating procedure. The first report of radiation is sent through command channels with "FLASH" precedence giving the location, intensity, and time the radiation was detected. Further reports are submitted in accordance with the unit standing operating procedure.

The intelligence officer has primary general staff responsibility for monitoring reports and the chemical officer actually processes the reports. The intelligence officer decides whether the monitoring reports give enough information to meet the commander's needs and, based on the chemical officer's recommendations, whether a radiological survey is required.

RADIOLOGICAL SURVEY. A radiological survey is the use of survey parties to determine the location, extent, and intensity of radiation throughout an area. Survey parties cover the area of operations and report intensities, location, and time of reading at key or measured points along a route. In aerial surveys, aircraft fly at the lowest possible constant altitude and speed along prescribed courses. The courses selected should be along easily identifiable checkpoints. Readings are taken at equal time intervals along the course and the location, altitude, intensity, and time of reading reported. Tests have indicated that readings should be taken below 500 feet for adequate reliability. If possible, air-to-ground correlation factors are determined for each aircraft for each survey. Use of helicopters simplifies air-to-ground correlation and gives access to terrain not possible for fixed wing aircraft.

The primary method of radiological survey is a centrally controlled operation planned and coordinated by the lowest headquarters having a chemical officer. The reporting channel for this type of survey is preferably from the survey party directly to the headquarters ordering the survey.

The alternate method for conducting a radiological survey is a decentralized operation directed through normal command channels. For example, within an Army division a battle group or combat command may be directed to conduct a survey of a given area. The battle group or combat command commander selects one or more companies to conduct the survey. The companies form survey parties from their monitor personnel. A company control party composed of an officer and necessary communications personnel controls the company survey parties. The battle group or combat command intelligence officer coordinates the operations when more than one company is involved. Reports from survey parties preferably go directly to the division headquarters but may be channeled through the headquarters of the battle group or combat command.

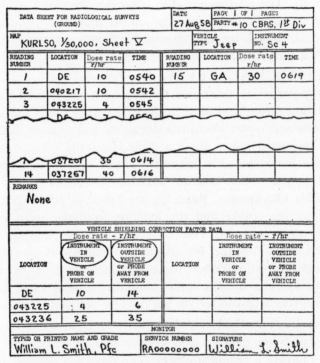

Figure 11. Ground radiological survey report form.

SUMMARY

In summary, sources are the actual origin of information and collection agencies are those who collect or process information— or both. Methods of collecting information include reconnaissance,

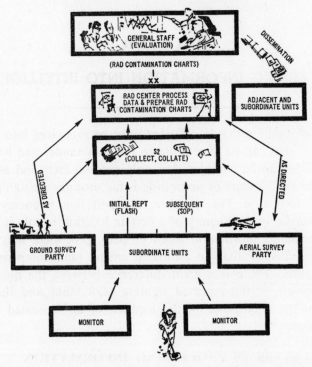

Figure 12. Flow of radiological monitoring and survey information.

combat surveillance, and radiological monitoring and survey. Imagination and ingenuity must be used to improve and develop new methods for collecting information. Above all, collection agencies report all information of intelligence value with the least possible delay even in the absence of specific instructions.

CHAPTER 4

PROCESSING INFORMATION INTO INTELLIGENCE

The information that is collected must be *processed* into intelligence before it can be of real use to the commander and his staff. Information can be considered as only random facts and assorted data. The end product of processing is the *meaning* or *significance* of the information. For example, a report that 8 enemy tanks were observed in the vicinity of a certain location is only information. The same information when properly processed, may result in the *intelligence* that an estimated enemy tank company is at that location. There is a great difference between the quality of a plan based on the reported sighting of 8 tanks and the plan based on the intelligence of the location of an estimated enemy tank company.

STEPS IN PROCESSING INFORMATION

Processing has three distinct steps: recording, evaluation and interpretation. Before discussing the mechanics of these steps, it is well to point out that information is processed in accordance with its importance. Usually, information of the area of influence is processed before information of the area of interest. Also, all information received is processed even if the information is apparently not complete. At times, the intelligence derived from processing incomplete information may be essential. For example, because of the usual time lag between the occurrence of an event and its being reported, complete information of a fleeting target or movement of reserves may not be received until after the target has become dissipated or the reserves have moved. If time is available, a search is directed for the additional information required to complete, confirm, or refute the intelligence developed from incomplete information.

Recording, the first step in processing, is reducing information to some written or graphic form and grouping together related items of information. This grouping together is often called *collation*. Evaluation, the second step, is the judgment of whether the information is useful and accurate. Interpretation, the last step, is the drawing of conclusions as to the meaning of the evaluated information. In processing information, recording is usually first and is followed in turn by evaluation and interpretation. For urgent items, recording may take place at the same time as evaluation and interpretation—or afterwards. Evaluation and interpretation may be instantaneous and immediately followed by dissemination of the intelligence produced. For example, a reliable source—an aviator—reports that 40 enemy tanks accompanied by about 20 armored personnel carriers are moving rapidly toward the friendly positions. There is no reason to doubt the accuracy of the report. The intelligence that an enemy infantry-tank attack is imminent is disseminated without delay. The recording of this information may have proceeded to the extent that it did not interfere with the dissemination of the intelligence. In this situation, recording is of secondary importance.

RECORDING

Proper recording makes available all information on a specific subject in a convenient form. This makes interpretation much easier. The importance of recording cannot be overstressed. Too often recording has been neglected with disastrous results. There have been many instances where a vital item of information was at the headquarters but, because of poor recording, was not available to those who needed it. Thorough recording can lead to production of outstanding intelligence. The story is told of the Swiss journalist who, in his daily column during World War II, was amazingly accurate in his news of movements of German units. Allied intelligence officers were convinced that the columnist had access to sources on the German General Staff. After World War II, the Swiss columnist explained that his success in accurately predicting troop movements was based on careful recording. He subscribed to a large number of German newspapers and had clerks carefully catalog every news item about German military forces. By examining all the items about a specific unit, he could draw logical conclusions. His deduction that the X Panzer Grenadier Division had moved from the Eastern Front to the Munich area for rest and refitting was based on the examination of two newspaper clippings. One clipping was an announcement that Hitler, before returning to Berlin from a visit to the Eastern Front, had personally decorated the Commander and other personnel of the X Panzer Grenadier Division. The next clipping, dated two weeks later, reported that the Commander of the X Panzer Grenadier Division, accompanied by his regimental commanders, had attended a gala concert given by the Munich symphony orchestra.

The grouping together of information of enemy activities helps brings into focus changes that cannot be noticed from examination of individual items of information. By plotting (one form of recording) similar activities on one overlay, significant changes become easier to detect. An army of any considerable size, for example, requires large amounts of supplies. For sustained operations these supplies are built up in forward areas in accordance with a transportation plan that takes time to execute. Regardless of enemy efforts to hide his movements, in the long run it is his main effort that will have the greatest supply build-up. Proper recording of all transportation activities—rail, motor, animal, and porter—should indicate the location of the main effort. Another example of where proper recording assists in indicating a trend is the redisposition of artillery. It takes from several days to several weeks to redispose artillery for either an offensive or a sustained defense. This process cannot be done instantaneously because of the requirements for survey, communications, ammunition supplies, and other facilities required by modern complex equipment. Once started, redisposition cannot be stopped or slowed down without endangering the success of the entire tactical plan. Overlays of located artillery weapons, compared with transportation overlays, give significant indications of the area and nature of future operations. Proper recording of other similar activities helps confirm trends in enemy actions and reduces the possibility of being victimized by an enemy cover and deception operation.

The most common aids used for recording are the intelligence journal, the enemy situation map, the intelligence worksheet, and intelligence files. Those aids that are used should require the least amount of time for recording and the least number of clerks.

INTELLIGENCE JOURNAL. The intelligence journal is a permanent and official record of all reports, messages, and important events. It is an index, or log, of intelligence activities in the order in which they occurred during a 24-hour period. The Army, Navy, and Air Force all require each unit and general staff section to keep a journal of its activities on a standard journal form. The journal, with its supporting documents, is used to keep other staff sections informed and to furnish part of the unit history and command report.

ENEMY SITUATION MAP. The enemy situation map is a temporary graphic record which shows current enemy dispositions and activities. Friendly information on this map is limited to that necessary to make the enemy information more meaningful. The friendly data usually posted are boundaries; location of command posts of higher, lower, and flank units; reconnaissance units; and the trace of the forward edge of the battle area. The information is best shown on an acetate overlay. The map itself is permanently marked to show the relief and drainage. Appendix XIII explains methods used to show relief and drainage.

Different categories of enemy activities are best shown on the enemy situation map by using separate overlays. For example, one overlay may show fortifications, another may show potential nuclear targets, another may show artillery dispositions, and so forth. In plotting enemy activities and dispositions, the last time the activity was observed or the disposition confirmed is shown. The enemy situation map and accompanying overlays should be clear and not require lengthy explanation. To prevent them from becoming cluttered, a number may be placed at the map location of the activity or installation and the explanation, with a corresponding number, at the side of the map or overlay. In addition to conventional signs and symbols, simple additional ones may be invented, if needed, and explained in a legend.

A detailed enemy situation map of scale 1:50,000 or 1:100,000 is usually kept at a division for the area to the immediate front.

The general enemy situation is usually posted on a map of scale 1:250,000. This map should not duplicate the information on the other map. In addition, it is convenient to keep a separate map that shows all information that affects the movement of units. This map includes information on roads, trails, bridges, streams, obstacles, minefields, cross-country trafficability, fallout, and similar features. Annotated mosaics are also posted as helpful map supplements. During rapid operations it is best to concentrate on keeping one enemy situation map up-to-date.

INTELLIGENCE WORKSHEET. The intelligence worksheet —or G2 worksheet—is another aid in recording and sorting information. The worksheet is a form of indexed catalog frequently kept as a loose-leaf notebook or card file. Specialized worksheets are usually maintained by each branch of the intelligence section at corps and higher headquarters. Intelligence worksheets are tem-

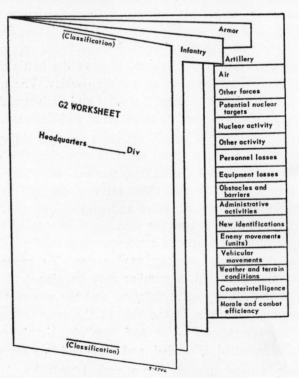

Figure 13. Typical division G2 worksheet.

porary records that are not sent out of the intelligence section. A common form of the worksheet is shown in figure 13.

Information from incoming messages and reports is entered in the worksheet under appropriate headings. At division headquarters the headings usually correspond to the paragraphs of the intelligence summary (ISUM). At corps and higher headquarters the headings usually correspond to the paragraphs of the periodic intelligence report (PERINTREP). (The ISUM and PERINTREP are discussed in chapter 5.) A message containing information on several subjects results in several entries, none of which quotes the entire message. For example, extracts from a message containing information on the locations of enemy reserves and artillery units are entered under "Reserves and Reinforcements" and "Artillery." Entries based on incoming messages include reference to the journal serial number of the message. For example: *"J23. 040730 Jun, from Div Avn Co: 5 stationary enemy medium tanks, poorly camouflaged, sighted at south edge of HERMA woods (248564)."* "J23" refers to the journal serial number. The date-time group entered refers to the time the event occurred. To be of most use, the worksheet must be kept up-to-date and obsolete entries promptly removed.

INTELLIGENCE FILES. Intelligence sections also maintain other files as are necessary to allow ready access to all available information. The most common of these files are the journal file, the information or reference file, and order of battle files. The *journal file* contains a copy or record of each message or document entered in the intelligence section journal. The *information or reference* file is a cross-index file of all information of possible future value. The form and content of this file depends on the needs of the unit. Because of the large volume of information filed at field army and higher headquarters, electronic data processing and punch card machines are used where possible. Order of battle files are kept in the same general manner and are usually based on the order of battle factors described in appendix II.

EVALUATION

Evaluation is the critical judgment of information to determine whether it is pertinent and how much weight it can be given.

PERTINENCE. Pertinence is important because it determines whether the information should be disseminated at once without waiting for further processing or even if it should be further processed. The value of the intelligence resulting from processing depends to a degree on how much weight the information can be given.

Judgment of the pertinence of an item of information depends on the answers to the following questions:

Is it information of the enemy or the area of operations?

Is the information needed immediately, and if so, by whom?

Is the information of possible present or future value, and if so, to whom?

Information not considered pertinent is not processed any further. Before deciding that information is not pertinent, the needs of other headquarters must be considered. If there is any doubt, the information should be disseminated to those headquarters that may possibly need it. Information that is needed immediately by other headquarters is sent to them without delay before the completion of processing. Some information may be disseminated before any evaluation and interpretation. For example, to speed up production of intelligence on nuclear targets, a commander may order that all information concerning *specified* enemy units, areas, or activities be reported immediately without any processing at any lower headquarters. Information not of immediate concern, but of possible present or future value is usually completely processed before dissemination.

RELIABILITY AND ACCURACY. The weight given to an item of information depends upon an evaluation of the reliability of the source of the information and the agencies that collected it and on the accuracy of the information. The principal basis for determining the *reliability* of a source and a collecting agency is previous experience. Experience with a particular enemy will indicate the general reliability of prisoners of war as sources of information. Members of some enemy units or nationalities may prove to be generally more reliable sources than members of other units or nationalities. Knowledge of the training, experience, and past performance of troop units helps judge their reliability as collecting agencies. Some units are soon recognized as having a tendency to exaggerate while others may have a tendency to be overly cautious in the information they report. Until experience is built up with the reports of a particular unit, all friendly collecting agencies are considered to be reliable. The final test in judging reliability is to decide whether the information could have been obtained under the conditions existing at the time.

Judgment of *accuracy*, or probable truth of the information, is based on the answers to the following questions:

Is the reported fact or event at all possible?

Is the report consistent within itself?

Is the report confirmed by information from other sources or agencies?

Does the report agree with other available information, particularly information known to be true?

If the report does not agree with other available information, which is more likely to be true?

The best way to judge accuracy is by comparison with other information. In doing this, care must be taken to ensure that the information compared comes from truly different sources and agencies. At times information derived from the same source may reach the headquarters through different channels. This often occurs when information is disseminated to adjacent units at the same time that it is forwarded to the higher headquarters that also commands the adjacent units. Regardless of source, the accuracy of information is reevaluated at each headquarters. The intelligence officer at a higher headquarters with more sources of information can better judge the accuracy of information than a subordinate headquarters with fewer sources.

The evaluation of an item of information is shown by a standard system of a *letter for reliability* and a *number for accuracy*. Evaluation ratings are made by the headquarters closest to the source; in tactical units this is usually the battle group or equivalent. A partial evaluation rating may be given if the information is incomplete. Because the agency closest to a source of information is ordinarily the best judge of the reliability of the source, a higher headquarters normally judges only the reliability of the head-quarters reporting the information.

The reliability of the source and agency is indicated as follows:

A—Completely reliable.

B—Usually reliable.

C—Fairly reliable.

D—Not usually reliable.

E—Unreliable.

F—Reliability cannot be judged.

An evaluation of "A" for a source is assigned only when the source is known to have long experience and extensive background with the type information reported. A "B" rating is used for sources of known integrity. Agencies are usually rated A, B, or C. When the source of the information and the collecting or reporting agency are evaluated differently, only the lower reliability rating is shown.

The accuracy of an item of information is indicated as follows:

1—Confirmed (by other sources or agencies).

2—Probably true.

3—Possibly true.

4—Doubtfully true.

5—Improbable (probably untrue).

6—Truth cannot be judged.

The letters and figures used to indicate the evaluation of an item of information are independent of each other. A completely reliable source may report information which is known to be improbable (rating A-5). A known unreliable source may report confirmed information (Rating E-1). A report evaluated as F-6 should not be discarded arbitrarily because it may later prove to be accurate. In disseminating information the evaluation follows each item. For example, "The division artillery of the Aggressor 102d Motorized rifle division has nuclear rounds of 2-KT yield (F-3)."

INTERPRETATION

Interpretation is the final step in processing and is the heart of the intelligence process. Interpretation determines the true meaning and significance of information. It is the use of critical judgment involving analysis (taking apart) integration (putting together), and formation of conclusions.

ANALYSIS. Analysis is the sifting and sorting of evaluated information to isolate those elements which have significance in respect to the mission and operations of the command. It requires good judgment and a thorough knowledge of the principles of military operations, the characteristics of the area of operations, and the enemy situation, including enemy doctrine and past practices. The enemy's routine habits, personalities, and reactions must be so well understood that the unusual activity, either positive or negative, can be readily isolated and recognized. Analysis often involves detailed research and increases in difficulty as the volume of information increases. When the volume of information is great and many individuals are involved, each must clearly understand the mission of the command.

INTEGRATION. Integration combines the significant elements isolated in analysis and other known information to form a logical picture or *hypothesis* of enemy activities or the influence of the characteristics of the area of operations on the mission of the command. The development of hypotheses requires judgment and the same background knowledge used in analysis. Hypotheses based only on what is logical according to the friendly doctrine are avoided because military operations follow a systematic pattern executed in accordance with *the doctrine peculiar to any given army*. While execution of tactical doctrine is subject, within limits, to the interpretation of the individual commander, the variations are quite minor. Discipline and military education lead to fairly uniform execution of operations in accordance with the doctrine taught by an army.

Each hypothesis is analyzed to determine the indications that should exist if the hypothesis is valid. The hypothesis is then tested by checking, within the limitations of the available time and means, to see if these indications exist. In formulating hypotheses, preconceived opinions are avoided by formulating and testing more than one hypothesis. Depending on the nature of the problem, integration may be a mental process, completed in a few moments, or it may be lengthy and involve the collection of a large volume of additional information.

CONCLUSIONS. The last step in processing is forming conclusions from the hypothesis considered valid. The conclusions should give the significance and meaning of the information in relation to the enemy situation and the area of operations.

EXAMPLE OF INTERPRETATION. The steps in interpretation can be illustrated in the following simplified example.

INFORMATION REPORTED:

The intelligence officers of two battle groups report that their units are receiving a large volume of mixed cannon fire including high bursts of very heavy cannon. Exact height of bursts unknown (A-1).

ANALYSIS (isolating the significant elements):

Very heavy cannon fires with high bursts.

High burst of very heavy cannon fire mixed in with large volume other cannon fire.

High burst registration on two battle groups.

INTEGRATION (combination with other known information):

This is the first report in 3 weeks of enemy use of very heavy cannon.

The enemy usually uses a high burst registration before firing a nuclear weapon by very heavy cannon.

The enemy seldom shifts his fires after high burst registration.

The enemy has used toxic chemicals in the same areas where he has used nuclear weapons.

FIRST HYPOTHESIS (logical explanation based on enemy doctrine and practices):

Aggressor is preparing to fire one or more nuclear weapons by very heavy cannon, possibly accompanied by a toxic chemical attack, and probably delivered within the division sector. He may also be registering away from the ground zero of his target. The high burst fire of very heavy cannon artillery is consistent with his previous practices and is logical. The large volume of other cannon fires is a means of masking the high burst fires.

SECOND HYPOTHESIS:

Aggressor is practicing deception and is trying to create the belief that he will fire a nuclear weapon. Aggressor has not in the past used this type of deception measure. This does not mean that he will never use it.

Conclusion (significance of the information in relation to the situation):

Aggressor is preparing to fire one or more nuclear weapons by very heavy cannon, probably within the division sector, and possibly accompanied by a toxic chemical attack. The risk is too great to support the deception hypothesis but the deception possibility should be pointed out to the commander and a search made for other evidence to prove or disprove it.

After the processing of each new item of information, the resulting intelligence is incorporated into the current intelligence estimate. Previous conclusions may be altered or confirmed, new enemy capabilities may be determined, and old ones dropped, and the relative probability of adoption of enemy courses of action should become clearer. The preparation of the intelligence estimate is discussed in the next chapter.

SUMMARY

In summary it can be said that processing converts raw information into intelligence. The steps in processing are recording, evaluation, and interpretation. The application of these steps requires a thorough understanding of the principles of intelligence operations and of the enemy.

CHAPTER 5

USE AND DISSEMINATION OF INTELLIGENCE AND INFORMATION

USE

The use of intelligence is the justification of all intelligence activities. Intelligence is used in arriving at decisions, primarily for improving the quality of the decision. Good intelligence allows a commander to accomplish more than would otherwise be possible, and to carry out his mission more efficiently. Intelligence is also required by all members of the staff as a basis for their analyses and plans. For these purposes, intelligence of an area usually provides a firm basis for decisions and plans, while intelligence of the enemy, uncertain to varying degrees, is used to assist in selecting a course of action.

To be of use, intelligence—and information as well—must be timely and reach the user in a useful form.

DISSEMINATION

Getting intelligence and information to the user is known as dissemination. The means and methods used in dissemination depend on the volume, urgency, and intended use of the material. Consideration is given to the needs of the user, his capability to handle the disseminated material, and the communication means available. Small units should not be overloaded with intelligence and information that are beyond their capacity to handle. Dissemination within a headquarters is usually made by oral spot reports, briefings, and distribution of written reports sent to and received from other headquarters. The intelligence officer not only produces and disseminates intelligence, but also advises on its use. Some means used for disseminating intelligence, such as the intelligence estimate and the analysis of the area of operations, embody some use of intelligence to assist in the preparation of commanders' and staff officers' estimates.

METHODS OF DISSEMINATION. The usual methods of dissemination are spot reports, intelligence summaries (ISUM's), periodic intelligence reports (PERINTREP), analyses of the area of operations, and intelligence estimates. Dissemination of weather and climate information and intelligence is discussed in appendix IX. Dissemination of specialized intelligence and information such as photointerpretation reports, prisoner of war interrogation and translation reports, technical intelligence bulletins and summaries, order of battle books and handbooks, radiological contamination estimates and reports, and maps is discussed in appendix X. Special reports, with no prescribed format, are used for disseminating intelligence and information not readily included in the reports just mentioned, or that are voluminous or highly specialized. The important consideration is not the compliance with a particular format, but getting the intelligence and information to the user in time and in a usable form. A format has value only as long as it assists in accomplishing this.

SPOT REPORT. Spot reports are one-time reports containing intelligence or information requiring immediate dissemination. These reports have no prescribed format but should, as far as possible, answer the questions: *Who? What? When? Where?* and *How?*

INTELLIGENCE SUMMARY. An intelligence summary (ISUM) is a summary of the significant information developed during a specific period and the conclusions on enemy capabilities and vulnerabilities at the end of that period. Intelligence and information NOT required for operations are omitted. Important items are not held for the next ISUM but are disseminated as spot reports. ISUM's are normally prepared at division and higher headquarters, however, they may be required from lower units by the next higher commander. ISUM's are sent to the next higher headquarters, the next subordinate units, and adjacent units by the quickest means, usually teletype. The period covered by an ISUM is specified by the next higher commander. In combat, ISUM's usually cover 6-hour periods starting at midnight. Appendix XI shows the format for an ISUM and an example.

PERIODIC INTELLIGENCE REPORT. The periodic intelligence report (PERINTREP) is a more detailed summary of the intelligence situation and covers a longer period than the ISUM. It includes the enemy situation, operations, capabilities, vulnerabilities, characteristics of the area of operations, and counterintelligence. Details of friendly forces which may be of value to the enemy are NOT included in the PERINTREP. Other intelligence documents such as technical intelligence summaries, prisoner of war interrogation reports, translations of captured documents, and weather and climate summaries may be disseminated as appendices to the PERINTREP. The PERINTREP is concise, but complete, with maximum use being made of sketches, overlays, marked maps, and annexes. However, use of abbreviations and unnecessary references to map coordinates are avoided.

The PERINTREP is normally prepared at corps and higher headquarters. In a fast-moving situation, corps may not issue a PERINTREP. At field army, a PERINTREP is always issued. The PERINTREP is disseminated to the staff, adjacent units, and the next two higher and lower headquarters. The period covered by the PERINTREP is prescribed by the next higher headquarters. In combat, a PERINTREP normally is published every 24 hours with the ending time of the period selected so that the user has it in time for his daily planning. The PERINTREP is distributed by the most practicable means considering its volume and urgency, usually by liaison officers or messengers. Appendix XII shows the format for a PERINTREP and an example.

A *weekly intelligence summary* generally follows the format of a PERINTREP and serves to highlight trends that are useful in planning future operations and in processing current information. These summaries are usually issued at field army and higher headquarters.

ANALYSIS OF AREA OF OPERATIONS. The analysis of the area of operations brings out the effect of the characteristics of the area on the general courses of action that the enemy and friendly forces may adopt. This knowledge is essential for the commander's estimate and all staff estimates. Without a thorough understanding of the environment in which an operation is to be conducted, neither tactical nor administrative plans can be made intelligently. The area of operations profoundly affects the use of maneuver forces, firepower, and administrative support. An understanding of the effects of the area is also a key in determining enemy capabilities and their probability of adoption, and enemy vulnerabilities.

With modern warfare being more than a conflict involving shot, shell, and nuclear effects, the selection of military courses of action must consider the attitudes, activities, and resources of the inhabitants of the area as well as the physical features of the area. A study of an area restricted to the physical aspects of weather and terrain, which treats the nonphysical aspects as an afterthought, is faulty. Failure to recognize that war now also involves the attitudes of the people in the area may only lead to transitory victories. This is particularly true in this era of emergence from colonialism. To achieve successfully the ultimate purpose of war—the political aims—all commanders must consider the influence of the people of the area. Not to do so may result in failure or severe handicap of tactical operations, and even loss of the battle or war. It has long been recognized that under any form of war, the theater commander must consider the effects of the political and psychological aspects of the area of operations in making major decisions. Such decisions have marked political and psychological implications. However, these same requirements also exist at *all* tactical levels to different degrees. Certainly they were factors in the decisions of US battle group commanders in Lebanon in 1958 and of French regimental commanders in Algeria since 1957. Knowledge of the attitudes of the people in the area permitted the Chinese Communists to take actions to win support which materially assisted in their victory over the forces of Chiang Kai Shek.

The analysis of the area also covers the effects not only on tactics, but also on the administrative and combat support activities that influence the choice of courses of action. All tactical courses of action are based on administrative and combat support capabilities. The study must give the tactical commander and his staff an understanding of the influence of the area on administrative and combat support activities so that the feasibility of a course of action can be determined accurately. History has many examples of a course of action which led to defeat because of the unforeseen adverse influence of the area on administrative and logistical support activities. The experiences in Russia of Napoleon and Hitler are outstanding examples. In administrative support units it is equally important that the commander weigh the effects of the area characteristics on his courses of action to carry out his mission and maintain the security of his command.

The analysis of the area of operations also considers the resources the commander uses in making up and carrying out courses of action. As new technological developments become available, the influence of the area on their battlefield use must be appreciated. For example, in determining the effects of the area on observation, not only is visual observation from the ground covered, but also observation by ground and airborne radar and infrared devices. In the past, the effects of the area on use of weapons was important only in relation to fields of fire. With new weapons systems, the effects on the delivery means must also be studied. Weather greatly influences use of some weapons. High, gusty winds affect the use of free rockets. Rain influences the use of certain fuzing devices. The commander must be aware of such effects because they will influence his choice of a course of action that depends on the use of certain weapons systems.

Taken as a whole, the analysis of the area of operations is a logical method for examining a particular problem to reach valid conclusions. The format is not rigid. The purpose is to give the commander and staff the information and intelligence of the area required for recommendations and decisions. The conclusions are the intelligence officer's interpretation of the effects of the characteristics of the area on enemy and friendly courses of action. Recommendations on actions to be taken as a result of the analysis do not come from the intelligence officer. These recommendations are made by other staff officers who *use* the analysis of the area of operations in preparing their estimates.

In preparing the analysis, the intelligence officer is assisted by other staff officers and the analyses made by higher headquarters. The engineer officer furnishes basic data on terrain. The supporting Air Weather Service unit furnishes weather and climate information. The chemical officer furnishes information on radiological contamination. Additional data is obtained from air photos, maps, strategic studies, and many other sources. In using the analyses of higher headquarters, caution is necessary. While these analyses are valuable sources of information, they may not be directly applicable. The intelligence officer studies and interprets all data in the light of *his* commander's mission. Of course, he consults with other staff officers in preparing conclusions and in selecting avenues of approach and key terrain features.

When possible, analyses are prepared for anticipated missions. These must be re-evaluated when the actual mission is received. The commander's decisions may require revision of the analysis because of the course of action selected. As the operation progresses, the analysis is revised as necessary with the uncovering of new areas and the receipt of additional or more accurate information. Written analyses are normally prepared at corps and higher headquarters in planning projected operations. At division headquarters, *written* analyses are usually prepared *only* for projected operations such as long-range amphibious or air-mobile operations.

Appendix XIII discusses the preparation of the analysis of the area of operations and includes an outline form and an exploded example. Appendix XIV discusses the influence of weather on army operations. Appendix XV discusses the influence of weather and terrain on nuclear effects.

INTELLIGENCE ESTIMATE. The most common—and most important—method for disseminating intelligence is the intelligent estimate. This estimate is an analysis of the area of operations *and* the enemy situation. In the estimate the intelligence officer determines:

Influence of the area of operations on friendly and enemy general courses of action;

Courses of action which the enemy can adopt and those he is most likely to adopt;

Enemy vulnerabilities that may influence the selection of friendly courses of action.

The estimate is oriented on the assigned or assumed mission. The influence of the area of operations on the friendly general course of action may be omitted if adequately covered in a current analysis of the area of operations. The significant facts of the characteristics of the area are analyzed to determine those which influence the choice of both friendly and enemy general courses of action and the major activities required to support these courses of action. If available, the conclusions of a current analysis of the area of operations are used for this purpose. After conclusions on the influence of the area of operations, the pertinent facts of the enemy situation are listed to provide an additional basis for the development and analysis of enemy capabilities. Based on the influence of the area and the enemy situation, the enemy capabilities are further analyzed to determine the enemy capabilities most probable of adoption, their relative probability of adoption, and enemy vulnerabilities. The intelligence estimate format is a framework for a logical and orderly examination of information and intelligence to arrive at conclusions. The essential thing is not slavishly following a format, but to give the commander intelligence of the area and the enemy required to arrive at decisions.

In preparing the intelligence estimate, the intelligence officer makes realistic assumptions and deductions. These are based on a thorough knowledge of the enemy and careful study of available information. Once assumptions and deductions have been made, action is taken to verify their accuracy. In estimating enemy capabilities and potential targets, the intelligence officer considers in addition to the data posted on the enemy situation map, enemy traits, habits, doctrine, and the personalities of major commanders. In a situation where the available evidence is not sufficient to support a firm conclusion on the relative probability of adoption of enemy courses of action, the intelligence officer should so state. However, in these circumstances based on his general knowledge of the enemy and with such evidence as is available, he must also give his opinion as to the relative probability of adoption of enemy courses of action. Failure to do so is abdication of the intelligence officer's responsibilities.

An intelligence estimate is prepared and kept up to date at all headquarters. As the intelligence estimate is concerned with many variables, a change in any major factor requires a review of the

Figure 14. Presenting an oral intelligence estimate.

entire estimate. An up-to-date intelligence estimate can be presented at any time because the estimating process is never ended.

The intelligence estimate is presented by the intelligence officer as required by the commander, or when changes develop in the estimate that must be brought to the attention of the commander or members of the staff.

The intelligence estimate is usually presented orally. Written intelligence estimates are normally prepared for projected operations when time is available or when dissemination is required and oral presentation is not feasible, and when a historical record is desired. Oral and written presentations are brief without sacrificing important details.

In oral presentations, the use of terrain models, colored maps and overlays, charts, and similar aids is helpful. Information and intelligence that is common knowledge or obvious from the visual aids is not repeated. Where appropriate, mention is made of "no change" from the information or intelligence previously furnished.

Appendix XVI gives additional guidance in the preparation of the intelligence estimate, a format, and an example.

Chapter 6

PLANNING THE COLLECTION OF INFORMATION

The famous Chinese writer on warfare, Sun Tzu, wrote centuries ago, "What enables the wise sovereign and the good general to strike and conquer and achieve things beyond the reach of ordinary men is foreknowledge.*" The foreknowledge or timely intelligence Sun Tzu wrote about just does not happen. It must be planned. Units do not provide the information needed when it is needed unless they are properly directed. This chapter describes the basis for that proper direction. As brought out in the last chapter, intelligence operations must be carefully planned. Without proper planning, the information collected will not be useful in producing useful and timely information.

There are three steps in planning for the collection of information. The first step is to determine what intelligence is required. The next step is to decide the priority in which the necessary intelligence items are required, that is—what comes first. The last step is to assign collection tasks properly among those agencies available to collect information. When these steps are completed, planning for the collection of information ends with the issuance of orders and requests to those who can furnish information, or will collect it.

WHAT INTELLIGENCE IS NEEDED?

As explained in the last chapter, intelligence requirements are determined by careful analysis and understanding of the problem on hand. What are the usual intelligence requirements? Generally, in tactical units, intelligence is required as a basis for decisions and plans concerning schemes of maneuver, selections of targets, and effects of fires (damage assessment). In any type of unit, intelligence is required to assist in processing other information and as

---

The Art of War by Sun Tzu Wu, page 96. Military Service Division, The Stackpole Company, Harrisburg, Pa.

a basis for measures to prevent being surprised by the enemy and to deny information to the enemy.

To produce the intelligence to meet those requirements, it is necessary to collect information *about enemy units and objects* and their activities, *the terrain, weather,* and the *non-physical characteristics of the area of operations.* The information is obtained from studies and direct observation of the enemy and the area of operations. Information of the non-physical characteristics of the area, such as attitudes and composition of the population, is usually obtained by analyzing information that had been collected over a period of time for use in strategic intelligence.

THE ENEMY. Information of enemy units and objects should cover their existence, nature, size, location, and activity (kind direction, rate of movement). Unfortunately, it usually is not possible to obtain by direct observation all this information. Sometimes it is possible to get complete information from one observer on weapons firing and small contaminated areas. However, it is rare that an observer can report, for example, that he has a division under observation. To detect a division, deductions must be made from the analysis of reports of many detectable items such as movements of personnel and vehicles, electromagnetic radiations (light, heat, radio, and radar), road networks, and breaches of camouflage discipline. Ordinarily, only the very simplest things and activities can be directly observed or detected. The greater the effects of a tactical weapon, the less likely it is to directly observe a suitable target for that weapon. The types of objects, activities, and terrain that can be observed and the typical requirements of certain Army headquarters for this information are shown in figure 15.

In planning the collection of these items of information, the factors below must be considered. The application of these factors vary with the command and its operations. The principle that all commanders do not require the same intelligence applies.

COVERAGE: Extent of area to be covered.

DETAIL: Scope and type of information required. For example, the field army is concerned with the locations and activities of

	Personnel (moving and stationary)	Vehicles (ground, air, moving, stationary, including projectiles and missiles)	Weapons (moving, stationary, firing)	Structures	Terrain	Electromagnetic radiations (communications, radar, heat, and light)	Nuclear explosions	Contaminated areas (radiological, chemical, and biological)
COVERAGE	Entire area	Entire area	Entire area	Entire area	Entire area	Entire area	Entire area	Entire area
DETAIL	Individual to 5,000 meters; squad size groups beyond[1]	Individual vehicles[1]	Individual crew served weapons[1]	Individual structures[1]	Equivalent to 1:50,000-scale map[1,2]	Location, frequency, type, time, and purpose	Location, height of burst, yield, fallout, and rainout	Location, type, and intensity
	Platoon-size groups[2]	Small groups of 15-25 vehicles[2]	Missiles and artillery weapons[2,3]					
	Company-size groups[3]	Groups of 50-75 vehicles[3]	Missiles[3,4]	Groups of structures[2,3]	Equivalent to 1:100,000-scale map[3]			
	Battalion-size groups[3]	Large groups of vehicles[3]		Complexes[4]	Equivalent to 1:250,000-scale map[4]			
FREQUENCY	Continuous coverage[1]	Continuous coverage[1]	Continuous	6 hours[1]	Initial coverage as soon as possible. New coverage seasonal or about each 6 months	Continuous	Continuous	As required
	2-4 hours[2]	1 hour[2]		12 hours[2]				
	4 hours[3]	4 hours[3]		Daily[3]				
	Daily[4]	Daily[4]		Every 2 days[4]				

SPEED	Immediate[1] 30 minutes[2] 2 hours[3] 4 hours[4]	Immediate[1] 30 minutes[2] 1 hour[3] 4 hours[4]	Immediate[1] Immediate 1 hour[4]	30 minutes[1] 2 hours 6 hours[4]		Immediate	Immediate	Immediate
ACCURACY GENERAL LOCATION	25-50 meters[1] 300 meters[2] 500 meters[3] 2,000 meters[4]	25-50 meters[1] 300 meters[2] 500 meters[3] 2,000 meters[4]	25-50 meters[1] 300 meters[2] 500 meters[3]	10-25 meters[1] 300 meters[2] 500 meters[3] 2,000 meters[4]	100 meters[1] 300 meters[2] 500 meters[3] 2,000 meters[4]	50-100 meters[1] 100 meters[2] 500 meters[3]	Not applicable	Not applicable
ACCURACY SPOT LOCATION	Varies with the characteristics of available weapons				Equivalent to 1:50,000 scale map[1] — Equivalent to 1:100,000-scale map[2] — Equivalent to 1:250,000-scale map[3,4]	10-25 meters[1] 50 meters[2] 100 meters[3] 200 meters[4]	100 meters[1,2] 300 meters[3] 600 meters[4]	200 meters[1,2]

[1] Battle group only.
[2] Division headquarters only.
[3] Corps headquarters only.
[4] Field army headquarters only.

Figure 15. Typical information of the enemy and terrain needed by certain army commands.

divisions, but this information is based on information of battalions or smaller units.

FREQUENCY: The number of times that areas are to be searched during a given period. Searches are preferably made on an irregular schedule. Certain parts of the area may be covered more often than others.

SPEED: Time from detection to arrival of the information at the headquarters that can act upon it.

ACCURACY: General location is the accuracy useful for general intelligence purposes. Spot location is the accuracy needed for target analysis to select weapons. Spot location often requires

WEATHER INFORMATION	COMMAND AREA				
	COMPANY	BATTLE GROUP, REGIMENT SEPARATE BATTALION	CORPS, DIVISION	ARMY	COMM-UNI-CATIONS ZONE
1. Climatic Information					
a. Climatic summaries		X	X	X	X
b. Climatic studies		As required	As required	As required	As required
2. Weather Forecasts					
a. General					
(1) 3-5 day		X	X	X	X
(2) 48 hour		X	X	X	X
(3) 24 hour	X	X	X	X	X
(4) 12 hour	X				X
b. Special					
(1) 24 hour area flight		X	X	X	X
(2) Aviation route and terminal		X	As required	As required	X
(3) Nuclear weapons		X	X	X	X
(4) Radiological defense			X	X	X
(5) Severe weather	X	X	X	X	X
(6) For engineer officer			X	X	X
(7) For chemical officer			X		X
c. Long range trend			X	X	X
3. Weather Observations					
a. Current weather	As required	As required	As required	As required	As required
b. Airstrip observations		X	X	X	X
c. Ballistic observations			X	X	X
4. Weather Summaries	As required	As required	As required	As required	As required

NOTE: See Figure 33 and Appendix IX for contents of weather forecasts and climatic summaries and studies.

Figure 16. Typical weather information needed by certain army commands.

additional collection of information after the general location is obtained.

WEATHER. Information and intelligence of weather is required by all commanders. The specific weather information to be collected is based on the particular weather effects that influence the operations of the command or the enemy. The weather information that is collected is restated in terms of these effects. To tell a commander that it will rain is only interesting. What the commander needs to know is the effect the rain will have on his and the enemy's operations. Figure 16 shows typical weather information needed by certain US Army commands. The information is given in terms of various forecasts, studies, and summaries whose contents are given in appendix IX.

NON-PHYSICAL CHARACTERISTICS. Requirements for information of the non-physical characteristics of the area of operations vary with the command. For example, a field army, with its large territorial and administrative responsibilities, needs a lot of this type of information. These responsibilities impose an extensive requirement for information leading to detection of espionage, sabotage, subversion, and for detailed information of the economics, politics, sociology, and psychology of the area. The field army intelligence officer coordinates the collection of this information. However, the interpretation of this information to produce the specialized intelligence requirements of the special staff (engineer, quartermaster, etc.) is the responsibility of the special staff officer concerned. On the other hand, a corps or a division needs information on sociology, politics, economics, and similar subjects only if they directly affect the commander's and the enemy's operations.

TARGET ACQUISITION. Another type of intelligence required by tactical units is the product of what is generally called *target acquisition*. This type of intelligence is as old as the history of warfare. A caveman who desired to attack a foe by throwing a rock at him was "acquiring a target" when he determined his foe's location from observation of footsteps, broken twigs and similar signs. With the tremendous range of modern weapons and the fluid tactics of modern warfare, the planning of target acquisition is of extreme importance. The attack by nuclear weapons of a few well selected targets may bring rapid success on the battlefield.

What are the information and intelligence requirements to be satisfied by target acquisition? These requirements are the detection, identification, and location of ground targets for the purpose of target evaluation analysis, and effective use of weapons. *Detection* is finding out that a target exists. *Identification* is the nature, composition and size of the target. *Location* is the exact height, direction, and distance of the target in relation to a known point. The difference between target acquisition and other types of information collection is one of degree, rather than of kind.

Target acquisition planning starts with developing a list of potential targets suitable for attack. In selecting areas where such targets are probably located, factors such as the friendly mission, information of the enemy, the terrain, and enemy tactics and habits are considered. While combat surveillance covers the entire battle area, selected areas are searched more closely in order to detect signs of potential targets or to disprove their presence. Frequently potential targets, particularly for attack by nuclear weapons, are determined by piecing together seemingly unrelated bits of information and intelligence. It is often impossible to state that a single item of information or intelligence is useful only for target acquisition purposes. The same kind of information and intelligence used for target acquisition is also used in determining enemy capabilities and vulnerabilities.

PRIORITIES

With the general requirements for intelligence and information established, the first step in planning the collection of information is completed. The next step, as mentioned earlier, is to decide the priority of the required intelligence items. During any operation, any item on which adequate intelligence is not available may mean the difference between success and failure. However, complete, absolutely accurate intelligence and information will rarely be available for two reasons. First, the enemy will attempt to foil collection activities. Second, all commands are limited in what they can collect and, therefore, must be directed toward some definite intelligence objectives. This results in a need for priorities to properly direct the collection of information. For example, in planning an airborne operation, it is more important to determine first the suitable drop zones than it is to determine the enemy capability to use chemical warfare against the assault troops.

ESSENTIAL ELEMENTS OF INFORMATION. At different stages of an operation, from planning to completion, certain specific items of intelligence or information may be required by the commander in order to make a decision with an acceptable degree of confidence. These items represent information and intelligence of the area of operations and the enemy. At times, the available information and intelligence may be complete enough to permit the commander to arrive at a decision with adequate confidence. In such cases, the commander has no outstanding priorities in his intelligence needs. However, at no time will the available information or intelligence be so complete that *other requirements* for information or intelligence will not exist.

The unavailable items, or item, of information or intelligence necessary for the commander, *at a particular time,* to make a decision with an acceptable degree of confidence are called the *essential elements of information—EEI. EEI* may or may not be established, depending on the extent and accuracy of the available information and intelligence. When established, the *EEI* are the *highest priority intelligence* tasks for the command. The intelligence officer first assigns tasks to collect the information required to produce answers to the *EEI.* Any remaining collection capabilities are then used to collect information needed to produce intelligence of *other* enemy capabilities, vulnerabilities, and characteristics of the area that could also affect the accomplishment of the mission. The sum of the *EEI* and *other intelligence requirements* equals the intelligence needs of the commander to accomplish his mission. Other intelligence requirements also include information of the enemy and the area that must be collected for use in interpreting other information. For example, while information on the enemy method for numbering vehicles does not help a commander make a decision, it may help interpret other information.

Because *EEI* must vary with the situation and stage of the operation, they cannot be routine. The *EEI* of a tactical command at different stages of an operation may be:

PLANNING STAGE: *"What drop or landing zones exist in our objective area? Special attention to the TOBIASA area." "Will the enemy extend his exposed west flank? Special attention to * * *."*

COMPLETION OF PREPARATIONS STAGE: *"Will the enemy attack before (a specified time)? If so, * * *." "Will the enemy change his dispositions? If so, * * *."*

EXECUTION STAGE: *"What targets suitable for nuclear attack will develop in the zone of the main attack? Special attention to * * *." "Will the enemy reinforce? If so, * * *."*

AT ALL STAGES FOR A SPECIFIC OPERATION: *"Will the enemy initiate chemical warfare? If so, * * *."*

The fact that the unit standing operating procedures (SOP) prescribe an item of information or intelligence for collection does not prevent its being listed as an *EEI*. For example, an SOP may require all units to report immediately items such as "known or suspected nuclear targets or indications of their existence or development." Whether or not such items are in the unit SOP, they are listed as an EEI if they are of overriding importance to the commander *at the particular time. EEI* normally do not refer to information which can be obtained by reconnaissance of areas under friendly control.

Appendix XVIII discusses the development, form, and content of *EEI* and other intelligence requirements.

Before recommending *EEI* to the commander, the intelligence officer consults with other staff officers. In tactical commands, he coordinates most closely with the operations officer; in administrative support commands, most closely with the logistic officer. Because *EEI* are the basis for the highest priority collection tasks, they are announced either by the commander or by the intelligence officer after the commander has approved them. Usually, the number of *EEI* at any one time will not exceed 3 or 4, otherwise the efforts of those who collect will probably be spread too thin.

EEI are announced to subordinate, higher, and adjacent commands to inform them of the commander's highest intelligence priorities *as general* guidance. This information alerts them to the major intelligence needs of the command at that time. *EEI* that are no longer timely are canceled promptly and new *EEI* are announced. Only those *EEI* are announced to subordinate units for which they can collect information. For example, *EEI* on enemy air or nuclear capabilities are rarely announced by divisions and usually not by corps. Major commands subordinate to field army normally are not capable of collecting information that can be used for producing this type of intelligence. Some *EEI* are not announced to the command since the information and intelligence to answer them must be obtained from higher and/or adjacent headquarters.

ASSIGNMENT OF COLLECTION TASKS

Deciding on intelligence priorities completes the second step in collection planning, but announcement of *EEI* is not adequate guidance for those who collect information. Commanders and intelligence officers who complain they do not receive adequate information after announcement of *EEI* have failed to take the next step: assigning specific collection tasks. This step consists of deciding which *specific* items of information are to be collected, where they can probably be found, when and where they are to be reported, and who will do the collecting.

SPECIFIC ITEMS OF INFORMATION TO BE COLLECTED. The basis for deciding the specific items of information to be collected is the fact that every future operation must be preceded by preparatory activity. Typical of these activities are forward movement of units, stockpiling supplies, displacement of weapons, and construction of bridges. The examination of evidence of his activities, in spite of security measures, permits predicting what the enemy will probably do, whom he will use, and where and when he will use them. Enemy activities are also clues to the existence of targets, and other possible enemy vulnerabilities. These clues, known as *indications,* are defined as *any positive or negative evidence of enemy activity or characteristic of the area which points toward enemy vulnerabilities and the enemy* *adoption or rejection of a specific capability.* Indications also include conditions or circumstances which result from earlier actions and failures of the enemy to take certain actions. For example, the location of enemy reserves may favor the adoption of a particular capability or indicate the existence of a vulnerability. An enemy failure to construct bridges may indicate rejection of a specific capability.

Orders and requests for specific information are based on the indications which result from analyzing *EEI* and other intelligence requirements. The analysis consists of determining the conditions and activities that can be expected to exist if the enemy adopts or prepares to adopt a particular capability, or when a particular enemy vulnerability exists or develops. For example, an *EEI* or other intelligence requirement which asks, "Will the enemy attack?" is analyzed by determining the enemy activities which might exist during the preparation or launching of an attack. Such activities include forward movement of units and artillery and strengthening of counterreconnaissance screens. In making this analysis, the friendly activities and dispositions are also considered; for example, the location of friendly reserves is considered because it may favor an enemy attack in an area distant from those reserves.

A thorough knowledge of the enemy and the area are important in analyzing *EEI* and other intelligence requirements. Particularly valuable is a knowledge of enemy organization, equipment, tactics, logistical methods, personality of the enemy commander, and the probable enemy knowledge of the friendly situation. It is important to remember that while the principles of war are valid for all armed forces, tactics differ. Therefore, the analysis of *EEI* and other intelligence requirements must be based on enemy methods. With experience, all units build up lists of enemy activities peculiar to each indication. For the most effective use, this information should be exchanged among higher, lower, and adjacent units.

Collection agencies are given the responsibility to collect specific information and *not* the responsibility for determining indications. If location of enemy artillery in depth is an indication, collection agencies are ordered to report the locations, types, and calibers of enemy artillery in their zones. Units are not ordered to report whether or not the enemy artillery is located in depth. The intelligence officer, and not the collection agency, determines—on the basis of the collected information—whether the indication is substantiated. Collection tasks must specify the enemy activity, location, characteristic, and weather and terrain conditions to be reported. For example, forward movement of enemy reserves is often an indication of reinforcement. Analysis of road nets, location of enemy forces, and a thorough knowledge of enemy tactics indicates the routes the enemy will probably use and where collection effort should be concentrated. A specific order or request for information would then be, *"Report volume, type, and direction of traffic on the following roads: * * *."* In the case of an intelligence requirement like, "What obstacles exist in our zone?" streams, located by map study, are indications of possible obstacles. An appropriate order or request for information would be, *"Report width, depth, velocity, and conditions of banks and bottom of LEDA river between SARA and LESLI."*

AGENCIES TO BE ASSIGNED SPECIFIC TASKS. The next step in collection planning is to select the collection agencies to get the desired information. The factors of capability, suitability, multiplicity, and balance influence the selection.

Capability is the physical ability to collect information. A tank unit in reserve is not asked for identifications of enemy units in contact nor is an artillery unit asked for information which can be obtained only from prisoners of war.

Suitability is the proper use of the capabilities of collection agencies. For example, collection of information most easily obtained by foot patrols should not be assigned to tank units and ground units should not be used to collect information that can best be obtained by aerial reconnaissance.

Multiplicity is the use of more than one collection agency to collect information on the same item. This is necessary because evaluation of information is most accurate when information from different sources and agencies can be compared.

Balance is the avoidance of overworking some collection

agencies while not using others to their full capabilities. Balance is not as important as the other factors.

COLLECTION WORKSHEET. To assist in developing the specific orders and requests for information and supervising collection activities, a written collection worksheet is of great help. A good collection worksheet contains:

A listing of the intelligence or information items required, usually stated in the form of a simple question;

The indications that answer the questions;

The specific information needed to confirm or deny each indication;

The agencies available to collect information;

Place and time the information is to be reported, if not specified in the unit standing operating procedure;

A means to show the progress of the collection effort, and notes for future action.

Because planning and supervising information collection is continuous, the collection worksheet is under constant revision. It can be compared to a blackboard on which entries are frequently changed. A new worksheet usually is started only at the beginning of a new operation. The collection worksheet is supplemented, as required, with other worksheets and plans such as air and ground reconnaissance plans, observation plans, and surveillance capability overlays. Figure 17 shows one form of a col-

UNIT:

Period covered: From: _____   To: _____

(1) Essential elements of information and other required intelligence items	(2) Indications (analysis of items in column (1))	(3) Basis for specific orders or requests	(4) Agencies to be used						(5) Place and time at which information is to be reported	(6) Remarks
			List all available agencies to	be used in the	collection of	required information.				
List the EEI announced for the operation or period, and other required intelligence items, spaced sufficiently to permit entry in column (2) of all indications pertinent to each item.	List opposite each item in column (1) those indications which best provide an answer to the question asked or implied by each item.	List the specific information sought in connection with each indication.	Place an X under each agency that has or can get the information bearing on each indication. The agency (or agencies) finally selected to obtain the information is indicated by circling (X) except for SOP items for agencies under the control of the unit.						Place: Headquarters or staff section to which information is to be reported if other than the issuing headquarters. Time may be a specific time, periodically, or as the information is obtained.	Notes for future actions and to indicate progress of the collection effort.

Figure 17. A collection worksheet form.

lection worksheet. Appendix XIX covers the preparation of the collection worksheet and has an example of a partially completed collection worksheet.

ORDER OR REQUEST TO COLLECTION AGENCY. When the entries of a particular *EEI* or other intelligence requirement on a collection worksheet are completed or modified, the order or request for specific information is sent to the collection agency—usually as a fragmentary order. Of course, the wording of this order or request is not necessarily the same as it appears on the collection worksheet. These fragmentary orders must be given the proper security classification. A knowledge of the information that a force is collecting permits deduction on that force's intentions.

INTELLIGENCE ANNEX. As time permits, an intelligence annex to the unit operations order is used to give the complete up-to-date order for the collection of information. While the intelligence annex gives the latest intelligence, it is above all the commander's order on intelligence activities for the operation. Appendix XX gives an outline form for an intelligence annex, and an example.

SUPERVISION OF COLLECTING. Although sending out orders and requests for specific information completes planning the collection of information, supervision of collecting is essential. Proper supervision helps improve the quantity and quality of the information collected. By visits and reports, the commander and the intelligence officer keep informed on the plans of subordinate collecting agencies to carry out collection tasks. The intelligence officer promptly makes any necessary adjustments. For example, he may instruct units to change locations of ground based surveillance radars to ensure that there is adequate coverage along boundaries and other important areas. The intelligence officer, as part of supervision, ensures that collection activities affecting the interests of other staff officers and units are coordinated with them. To do this, he may require subordinate collection agencies to submit to him their plans for certain collection activities. The intelligence officer also checks administrative activities to be sure that they support the collection of information from sources such as prisoners of war and refugees.

SUMMARY

The process of planning the collection of information can be summarized as: determining what intelligence is needed, which is needed first, what information must be collected in order to produce the required intelligence, and who will collect the information. When this is done, the collection of the information must be properly supervised.

CHAPTER 7

COUNTERINTELLIGENCE

The famous military writer of antiquity, Vegetius,* wrote, *"A general is not easily overcome who can form a true judgment of his own and the enemy's forces."* An opposing general cannot be denied the information to form a judgment of his own forces. However, he can be denied the information of his opponent's forces. This is the task of counterintelligence. Counterintelligence is primarily the denial of information to the enemy. As explained in chapter 1, intelligence and counterintelligence operations go hand in hand and are inseparable. In addition to denying the enemy information of the friendly activities and intelligence operations, counterintelligence also includes prevention of enemy sabotage and subversion and the detection of disaffection within the friendly forces. Effective counterintelligence measures increase the security of the command and help achieve surprise. Surprise depends not only on reliable intelligence and rapid movements but also on proper counterintelligence measures. By denying information to the enemy, the risks of a command are reduced by decreasing the enemy ability to use his combat power effectively, particularly nuclear fire. By maintaining strict and effective counterintelligence measures, the German Army in late 1944 was able to mass forces for the Ardennes offensive despite the overwhelming fire superiority—particularly airpower—of the US and British forces. The prevalent overcast weather was coupled with effective counterintelligence measures to keep the massing of the German forces from becoming known to the US and British.

COORDINATING COUNTERINTELLIGENCE ACTIVITIES

The intelligence officer has staff responsibility for planning and directing counterintelligence measures. Dispersion on the nuclear

---

Military Institutions of the Romans, by Vegetius. Military Service Division, The Stackpole Company, Harrisburg, Pa.

battlefield and improved surveillance devices make it necessary that thorough counterintelligence measures support every aspect of combat and administrative support activities. In doing this, the intelligence officer coordinates with the rest of the staff to ensure that the activities they supervise are supported with proper counterintelligence measures. Coordination ensures that counterintelligence measures do not interfere unnecessarily with operational and administrative activities. For example, counterintelligence measures may restrict movements of vehicles and unintentionally result in delaying the build-up of supplies or resupply operations. Proper staff coordination prevents such a situation or provides the commander with adequate information on which to decide the relative importance, at the moment, of either slowing supply operations or denying information to the enemy. Every staff officer and subordinate commander, in effect, acts as a counterintelligence special staff officer. In that capacity, they advise on the counterintelligence aspects of their activities. For example, the transportation officer advises on the counterintelligence implications of transportation movements; the surgeon on the counterintelligence aspects of locations of medical installations. As discussed earlier, *all* activities in every armed force follow a definite pattern. Knowledge of these activities helps the enemy to determine the intentions of his foe.

THE SOLDIER. While all units are counterintelligence agencies and take the necessary steps to deny the enemy information of their activities and dispositions, the ultimate agency in this field is the individual soldier. Most counterintelligence operations depend on his ability to carry out proper security, camouflage, observation, and reporting procedures. Because prisoners of war are one of the most prolific sources of information, as part of counterintelligence it is essential that all personnel be thoroughly trained in evasion, escape, and resistance to enemy interrogation.

SECURITY UNITS. The complexity of counterintelligence operations at division and higher headquarters, requires that the intelligence officer have expert assistance in the overall guidance and coordination of intelligence measures. This assistance is furnished by the security personnel of the assigned or attached military intelligence unit described in appendix V. To be most effective, the personnel of the security sections and companies of these military intelligence units should be qualified in tactical counterintelligence measures as well as in measures used in the detection of spies, subversion, and prevention of sabotage.

OPERATIONS

Counterintelligence operations are classified generally as military security; civil security; port, frontier, and travel security; censorship; and special operations.

MILITARY SECURITY. Military security counterintelligence operations include all the activities to protect a unit from sabotage and subversion and to deny information to the enemy. In tactical units, these operations stress protecting nuclear delivery means and associated installations and neutralizing the enemy target acquisition effort. Typical military security counterintelligence measures are: the use of passwords; limiting the use of certain means of communication and other electromagnetic emitters; restricting movements; limiting access to vital installations; and counter-reconnaissance. While many of these measures are routine and are reduced to standing operating procedures, their importance cannot be neglected. Intercept of careless radio and telephone communications permitted the German Army to determine the order of battle of the US forces in France in 1944.

CIVIL SECURITY. Civil security counterintelligence operations include all the counterintelligence activities affecting the civilians in the area. These operations are extensive for commands with large territorial responsibilities in heavily populated areas, and in situations short of war. Typical civil security counterintelligence measures are control of circulation by curfews and passes, censorship, security screening of civilian labor, monitoring of suspect political groups, and industrial plant protection. Large numbers of civilians that can be expected to flee through battle areas from actual or expected nuclear fires or targets in the field army area, pose a great security problem. These refugees can serve as a cover for enemy agents and infiltrating forces. In the early period of the fighting in Korea in

1950, the Communists frequently used refugees for this purpose —with considerable success.

PORT, FRONTIER AND TRAVEL SECURITY. Port, frontier, and travel counterintelligence operations are military and civil counterintelligence measures for control of airports, seaports, land and sea frontiers, international air boundaries, and all non-military travel into and out of a theater. These operations include measures such as military travel permit systems, sea and land frontier patrols, and security screening and control of frontaliers (legal daily frontier crossers).

CENSORSHIP. Censorship is control of communications such as mail, telephones, news despatches, motion pictures and radio and television broadcasts, to prevent information of military value from reaching the enemy. It is accomplished by monitoring and examining all non-official communications.

SPECIAL OPERATIONS. Special operations include the specialized use of active and deceptive counterintelligence techniques and procedures in secret operations directed against hostile and unfriendly intelligence organizations and activities. Examples of these operations are compilation and dissemination of counterintelligence target data and operation of special centers for interrogating captured enemy agents.

DIVISION OPERATIONS

Division counterintelligence operations are primarily concerned with enemy target acquisition activities. Of particular concern are military security measures for protecting nuclear weapons systems. Typical of such measures are: restriction of access to installations, camouflage, displacement during conditions of reduced visibility, and use of misleading unit markings on vehicles of nuclear delivery units.

Divisions do not have organic counterintelligence specialists. However, such specialists are organic to the security section of the military intelligence detachment which is normally attached to a division. The senior officer of this security section usually is designated the chief of the counterintelligence branch of the division G2 section. When situations such as short of war or occupation duties require greatly increased attention to civil security or similar counterintelligence operations, the security sections attached to the division may require augmentation.

CORPS OPERATIONS

Corps counterintelligence operations are about the same as at division except that greater numbers of units and larger areas are involved. In addition, corps counterintelligence operations are also concerned with longer-range operations. Corps counterintelligence activities, in addition to protecting nuclear delivery systems and reducing the effectiveness of enemy target acquisition activities, may also include extensive civil security, frontier and travel security, and censorship operations. These operations are carried out to the extent necessary to ensure the security of corps operations. When such operations are required, the corps is augmented with additional counterintelligence specialists or military intelligence units. Typical of these activities are conduct of security checks in coordination with units handling refugees and other civilians arriving from areas under enemy control, and establishment of curfews and restrictions on circulation of civilians.

FIELD ARMY OPERATIONS

Field army counterintelligence operations are similar to those of corps and divisions. However, the operations are broader in scope because of the larger number of units, the larger areas involved, and longer-range planning. Field army counterintelligence operations involve extensive civil security and special operations. Counterintelligence operations pertaining to civil security are based on support of tactical operations and later transfer of territorial responsibility to the communications zone. Frequently, the field army conducts counterintelligence operations within corps areas. In such circumstances, the activities are coordinated with the corps intelligence officer to avoid duplication of effort and conflict. Theater army and communications zone counterintelligence personnel and units may be attached to the field army to assist in counterintelligence operations and to provide continuity when the communications zone displaces forward.

ARMY GROUP OPERATIONS

The army group has no territorial responsibilities and conducts only such counterintelligence operations as are necessary to protect the army group headquarters. Counterintelligence operations in support of army group cover-and-deception plans are usually assigned to subordinate units for execution. Counterintelligence plans of the army group usually take the form of policy guidance to coordinate the operations of subordinate units. Major emphasis is on security of military operations. This involves considering enemy activities which threaten military security countermeasures.

LOGISTICAL COMMAND OPERATIONS

In logistical commands, counterintelligence is usually the major activity of the intelligence personnel. Denying the enemy information of the supplies, service installations, nuclear weapons systems, and transportation and communication means, and their protection against sabotage, are vital to the accomplishment of a logistical command's mission. The large territorial responsibilities of the theater army logistical command headquarters require extensive counterintelligence operations of all types. Although they vary in scope and emphasis, the counterintelligence procedures of logistical commands are similar to those at tactical headquarters. Counterintelligence operations for security of staging and marshaling areas located within the communications zone are carried out by logistical command counterintelligence personnel. Logistical command counterintelligence operations are relatively static. Counterintelligence units are normally assigned responsibility for an area, locality, or installation and remain there as long as their services are required.

THEATER ARMY OPERATIONS

Theater army usually delegates its territorial responsibilities to the field armies and to the theater army logistical command headquarters. Theater army performs counterintelligence operations for security of the theater army headquarters and for missions not suitable for assignment to subordinate commands. Counterintelligence activities are usually confined to coordinating and supervising operations of subordinate commands and the administrative control of counterintelligence specialist personnel assigned to the theater. Theater army coordinates counterintelligence operations by announcing policies and supervising the activities of subordinate commands to ensure complete counterintelligence coverage.

PLANNING

All counterintelligence operations, like all other intelligence operations, require careful planning to be successful. Counterintelligence planning is based on enemy capabilities to collect information and to conduct sabotage and subversive activities. The products of this planning are counterintelligence countermeasures. These measures are designed to prevent the enemy from learning of those friendly dispositions and activities that disclose the commander's intentions and prevent the disruption of those required for the accomplishment of the mission. Counterintelligence planning in support of an operation begins with the inception of the operation plan, and continues until the operation is completed. The procedures used in counterintelligence planning are similar to the planning of the collection effort described in chapter 6.

COUNTERINTELLIGENCE ESTIMATE

To determine the enemy information collection, sabotage, and subversion capabilities, and their relative probability of adoption, the intelligence officer prepares a counterintelligence estimate. The estimate serves as a basis for developing counterintelligence measures. The estimate considers the impact of the enemy's collection, sabotage, and subversion activities on the friendly courses of action and the requirements for counterintelligence measures. A valid counterintelligence estimate must be based on knowledge of the order of battle of the enemy units and agencies that collect intelligence information and conduct sabotage and subversive activities. Particularly important are their organization, training, equipment, doctrine, techniques, and deployment.

With minor modifications, the intelligence estimate format is suitable for counterintelligence estimates. Normally, a written counterintelligence estimate is prepared only by field army and logistical commands of the communication zone. Usually, the counterintelligence estimate is prepared for the intelligence officer by the chief of the counterintelligence branch of the intelligence section. Appendix XXI shows a counterintelligence estimate format. A counterintelligence worksheet, similar to the G2 worksheet, is usually maintained at division and higher headquarters to assist in preparing counterintelligence estimates.

COUNTERINTELLIGENCE MEASURES WORKSHEET.

Based on the conclusions reached in the counterintelligence estimate, a counterintelligence measures worksheet is prepared or revised. This worksheet, similar to the collection worksheet, aids in counterintelligence planning and is the basis for preparing counterintelligence orders and requests. Figure 18 shows a counterintelligence measures worksheet form. Categories of counterintelligence operations involved (column 2) are listed to ensure completeness of planning. Appendix XXII shows a partially completed counterintelligence measures worksheet.

UNIT:
Period covered: From _____ To: _____

(1) Phases or periods of operation	(2) Categories of counterintelligence operations involved	(3) Counterintelligence measures to be adopted	(4) Agencies responsible for execution of counterintelligence measures	(5) Instructions regarding entries in columns 3 and 4, notes for future action, and staff co-ordination measures.

Figure 18. Counterintelligence measures worksheet form.

PASSIVE AND ACTIVE MEASURES

Counterintelligence measures are either passive or active. Passive measures conceal information from the enemy. They include measures such as secrecy discipline, security of classified documents, communications and electronic security, movement control, censorship, and electronic counter-countermeasures. Passive measures can usually be standardized and included in the unit SOP. Active counterintelligence measures actively block the enemy's efforts to collect information or to engage in sabotage or subversion. Such measures include counter-reconnaissance, counterespionage, countersabotage, countersubversion, and use of smoke to deny enemy observation. Active measures vary with the mission of the unit.

Counterintelligence orders and requests are prepared and transmitted in the same manner as orders and requests for specific information described in appendix XIX. Counterintelligence orders and requests are included in the intelligence annex to the operations order.

CHAPTER 8

SPECIAL OPERATIONS AND INTELLIGENCE

The intelligence operations described in the previous chapters generally apply to all military operations. This chapter discusses their application to certain *special operations* that are relatively new or of increased importance in modern warfare. Special operations are military operations conducted under special conditions or involving special methods. Examples of special conditions are unusually hot or cold weather or very mountainous or swampy terrain. Examples of special methods are tactical cover and deception operations, pyschological warfare, and electronic warfare.

In supporting special operations, certain aspects of intelligence operations are emphasized, depending on the nature of the extreme in weather or terrain or the nature of the special operational method concerned. For example, operations in extremes of weather and terrain require *very early* collection of *detailed* information of the extreme area characteristic and the determination of the effects on both friendly and enemy broad courses of action. Extremes of weather and terrain usually slow the collection and transmission of information and intelligence. Measures must be preplanned to overcome these difficulties. In special operational methods such as movement of assault troops by helicopters, determination of *air avenues of approach* and landing areas are of increased importance. In airborne operations, detail in the intelligence furnished to participating units is emphasized because they lack the background of details built up by continuous operations.

The specific special operations that will be discussed are: psychological warfare, unconventional warfare, tactical cover and deception, electronic warfare, chemical and biological warfare and air defense.

PSYCHOLOGICAL WARFARE

Psychological warfare is the use of propaganda and other actions to influence the opinions, emotions, attitudes, and behavior of enemy, neutral, or friendly groups to support the accomplishment of national aims and objectives. In peacetime, psychological warfare may be used to influence the minds of people to prepare them for participation in subversive activities when hostilities begin. Intelligence support of psychological warfare requires determining the enemy vulnerabilities, enemy capabilities, and characteristics of the area applicable to psychological warfare operations and the effectiveness of friendly and enemy psychological warfare operations. Intelligence on enemy military and civilian personalities and methods, derived from prisoners of war, refugees, and the enemy news media, assist in formulating psychological warfare plans and policies. Strategic intelligence studies, including the National Intelligence Survey (NIS), also provides valuable background information of the history and ethnic composition of the enemy.

Intelligence furnished in support of psychological warfare operations should include an analysis and evaluation of the reasons for the existence of enemy vulnerabilities to psychological warfare and nature of the vulnerability. For example, in seeking answers to a psychological warfare intelligence requirement based on the morale, discipline, and attitude of the enemy, typical questions considered are: "What will reduce his morale or change his thinking?" "Where is the enemy most vulnerable to psychological attack?" "What measures does he like and dislike (such as music or news broadcasts)?" "What are his problems, his worries, his fears?" "What are his living conditions?" and "Why does he fight or surrender?" In addition, intelligence on enemy capabilities for countering the friendly psychological warfare is also required.

UNCONVENTIONAL WARFARE

Unconventional warfare is conducted within the enemy's sphere of influence primarily using indigenous personnel and resources to achieve military, political, or economic objectives. Unconventional warfare includes guerrilla warfare, sabotage, subversion (resistance) against hostile states, and evasion and escape. Because large-scale unconventional warfare activities depend on the active and passive support of the population in the area, detailed intelligence of the political and economic factors influencing them is required. Support of the wrong political groups, poorly selected activities, and destruction of certain installations in the enemy rear area, can adversely affect the attitudes of the population and reduce the effectiveness of unconventional warfare operations.

GUERRILLA WARFARE. Guerrilla warfare is conducted within enemy-held territory by indigenous forces to reduce the combat effectiveness, industrial capacity, and morale of the enemy. Guerrilla operations normally are conducted by units organized on a military or para-military basis. These operations require intelligence of the nature and extent of support that can be expected from the local populace, capability of the enemy to combat the guerrillas and to protect guerrilla objectives, and availability of terrain favorable to guerrilla operations. In preparing this intelligence, strategic intelligence studies produced by the military services and other agencies such as the State Department and the Department of Commerce are very helpful. Air reconnaissance, prisoner of war and refugee interrogation, enemy communications intercepts, newspapers, and broadcasts are used to provide supplemental material and current information. The effects of guerrilla warfare operations are evaluated on the basis of information obtained by aerial reconnaissance of destruction, spies and informers, communication intercepts, prisoner of war interrogation, enemy countermeasures and reactions, reports from the guerrilla force and other means. This evaluation provides a basis for planning future guerrilla warfare activities.

ESCAPE AND EVASION. These activities assist friendly military personnel and other selected individuals in enemy-held or unfriendly areas to evade capture and to escape if captured. Information and intelligence are required on such items as suitable areas and enemy procedures for area control and search. The information and intelligence required to evaluate and improve escape and evasion plans are obtained from normal intelligence operations including interrogation of knowledgeable prisoners of war, refugees, and successful escapers and evaders. The intelligence officer analyzes this information and intelligence and *assists* the operations officer in preparing escape and evasion plans. The intelligence officer also coordinates counterintelligence measures and assists in the intelligence aspects of escape and evasion training.

TACTICAL COVER AND DECEPTION

Tactical cover and deception operations disguise friendly dispositions, capabilities, and intentions and mislead the enemy into actions that are disadvantageous to him and favorable to the friendly force. These operations are used to support tactical plans and operations and are kept up for a relatively short period. Tactical cover and deception includes feints, ruses, demonstrations, diversion, and holding attacks.

Tactical cover and deception has been practiced since the beginning of man. The wooden horse before the walls of Troy had its modern counterpart during the Nazi seizure of Norway in World War II, when the invading troops were concealed in seemingly harmless merchant ships. Technological advances in surveillance techniques open new opportunities in this field. The capability to detect infrared transmissions makes it possible to deceive by carefully placing simulators which produce in an infrared detector the same responses as tanks, trucks, and other combat equipment. Because of the tremendous destructive power of nuclear weapons, all armed forces search for indications of the locations of nuclear weapons, storage points, and launching sites. Opportunities to deceive in this field are many and varied. Real and false storage sites for nuclear components can be constructed under strict security measures. Some ordinary supplies may be moved under heavy guard with restrictions on the movements of civilians in the area, in order to portray the movement of warheads. Such measures may deceive the enemy as to which storage sites, movements of ammunition, or delivery means are false.

Tactical cover and deception is directed *toward the enemy commander and his staff*. It is intended for the attention of the enemy's regular intelligence organization in order to reach the desired audience. Psychological warfare is used to support deception operations by disseminating information which confirms or supports the deception story presented to the enemy through his intelligence channels. The success of cover and deception depends upon ability to predict the enemy probable reaction. To successfully do this, it is necessary to think as the enemy does and not how the friendly commander would react in the enemy situation. A thorough understanding of the enemy culture and military system is essential. To determine who must be deceived, the enemy command and intelligence organization must be known in order to establish where decisions and intelligence evaluations are made. The enemy characteristics and habits most susceptible to deception and those which present the least likely target for deception must be determined. The probable reaction of the enemy commander is most important. An uncertain commander may react to deception while a steadfast commander may completely ignore deception measures unless they are unusually convincing. Because some commanders may be overanxious and others overcautious, it is necessary to know the personal characteristic of the opposing commander.

In determining the enemy's susceptibility to deception, the probable accuracy of his knowledge of the situation at the time must be known. This also permits making the simulated situation appear realistic in the light of the enemy estimates of the friendly force. Usually the enemy is most susceptible to deception in those fields where his intelligence is poorest. These areas can be determined by interrogation of prisoners, determination of where the enemy information collection activities are concentrated, and communications intercepts.

Tactical cover and deception calls for strict secrecy and adequate counterintelligence measures. Information of cover and deception operations is disseminated strictly on a need-to-know basis. Arousing the suspicion of the enemy may result in the enemy concentrating his collection effort and lead to disclosure of the plan. Units and individuals should, as far as possible, be kept unaware that they are participating in a cover and deception operation. This helps maintain an atmosphere of realism and decreases the chance of the operation being compromised. Continued success of tactical cover and deception operations also depends in part on convincing the enemy that his failure was due to faulty evaluation of information. Therefore, the pattern of intelligence activities is continued after the tactical cover and deception operation is ended.

The operations officer has staff responsibility for the planning and execution of tactical cover and deception operations. The intelligence officer is the major contributor of information and intelligence on which cover and deception plans are based and their effectiveness measured.

ELECTRONIC WARFARE

Electronic warfare (EW) is the military use of electronic devices and techniques to prevent or reduce enemy effective use of radiated electro-magnetic energy while ensuring the effective use of such energy by the friendly force. Electronic warfare was used to some extent during World War II. At that time, there were no specific units to conduct electronic warfare nor was it particularly emphasized. Operations in this field were conducted as the need became apparent. For example, the British used electronic warfare successfully against the German bomber command electronic guidance systems during the "Battle of Britain." Electronic warfare has grown in importance because of widespread dependence on electronic systems for communications, air navigation, and missile guidance.

COUNTERMEASURES AND COUNTER-COUNTERMEASURES. Electronic warfare is subdivided into electronic countermeasures (ECM) and electronic counter-countermeasures (ECCM). Electronic countermeasures are actions taken to prevent or reduce the effectiveness of enemy equipment and tactics using or affected by electromagnetic radiations. Passive electronic countermeasures determine the existence, source, and pertinent characteristics of enemy electromagnetic radiations, and include the collection and technical analysis of electronic intercept information for immediate tactical use. Active electronic countermeasures are electronic jamming and deception. Electronic counter-countermeasures are actions taken to ensure effective use of electronic radiations despite the enemy's countermeasures.

CAPABILITIES. The major capabilities of electronic warfare from an intelligence point of view are: jamming enemy radio nets; blinding, or presenting false information to enemy electronic equipment, organization, and locations. All of these capabilities cannot be accomplished simultaneously. Even partially successful electronic warfare operations can produce valuable information or severely impede an enemy operation at a critical time. The overall implications of electronic countermeasures must be considered in planning electronic warfare operations. The undesirable effects of jamming on friendly electronic systems and communications intelligence sources are weighed against possible diversion of enemy resources to evade the jamming as well as the immediate tactical advantages to be gained. The estimated benefits determine whether requirements for intelligence take priority over jamming operations.

ACQUISITION PHASE. The intelligence acquisition phase of electronic warfare is the gathering, evaluating, and interpreting of information of enemy electronic devices; determining the frequencies on which such devices operate; how and where they are operating; and any vulnerabilities of the equipment. This phase, which includes both passive electronic countermeasures and electronic intelligence, is the foundation for further electronic warfare operations. This phase is continuous and fills the need for technical information on which to base research for equipment and systems improvement. For example, as new enemy equipment is brought into use, its characteristics must be learned rapidly in order to build a counter device to jam, blind, reduce its reliability, or otherwise make it ineffective. As enemy equipment is located it may be attacked by fire or by electronic warfare operations.

FIELD USE. The field use of electronic warfare includes the tactical search for electronic warfare targets (passive electronic countermeasures) which electronic intelligence has previously identified. This is performed by electronic warfare units which, once the targets are located, take active electronic countermeasures against them. Active electronic countermeasures counter (jam, blind, deceive, redirect, or prematurely detonate) enemy electronic communication nets, detection devices, guidance systems, or fuzing systems. Active countermeasures which are closely allied to tactical cover and deception operations are coordinated by the intelligence and operations officers.

ANTIJAMMING. Defensive electronic warfare operations include electronic counter-countermeasures (ECCM) or antijamming. These operations are coordinated by either the intelligence or operations officer, depending on the use of the equipment involved. Electronic counter-countermeasures include reducing vulnerability to jamming by dispersing communications and surveillance equipment, using reverse slope positions and frequent displacement. Another electronic counter-countermeasure is reducing the use of communication and surveillance equipment by such measures as periods of listening silence. This hampers enemy signal intercept and other collection operations. Still another measure is to use alternate communication and surveillance equipment operating on different frequencies and from different locations. Operator training in antijamming techniques and ability to detect enemy deceptive action against friendly devices is also an effective measure.

SCOPE OF EFFORT. The electronic intelligence collection effort must be continuous, widespread, and long-range in nature. Continuous surveillance over enemy electronic systems is maintained by all available means including special supporting agencies. A knowledge of the locations, characteristics, purpose and place of electronic systems in the enemy order of battle structure is necessary for decisions on *whether, when* and *how* they can best be countered.

ENEMY ELECTRONIC WARFARE MEANS. The intelligence officer provides the necessary intelligence of the enemy electronic systems upon which electronic warfare plans are based. He ensures the efficient employment of all available collection agencies in order to develop intelligence of the enemy's electronic warfare means. This intelligence, incorporated in his continuing estimate, includes both the enemy offensive and defensive electronic warfare capabilities.

CHEMICAL AND BIOLOGICAL WARFARE

Chemical and biological warfare give the commander weapons effective over large areas. Unlike nuclear weapons, chemical and biological warfare do not destroy facilities and equipment but attack the operating personnel. Chemical warfare is the use of toxic chemicals, flame, smoke, or incendiaries. Biological warfare is the use of living organisms, or their toxic products, to produce disease or death of men, animals, or plants. Biological warfare includes the use of chemicals to cause harm to plants.

USE. Toxic chemical agents can be used to cause either heavy casualties or area contamination. Quick acting, *nonpersistent* toxic chemical agents produce heavy casualties, but the contamination generally disappears in several hours or less. *Persistent* toxic chemical agents produce casualties and may also be used to deny terrain features and areas. These agents dissipate slowly and may present a skin contact hazard for several days, thus limiting the use of contaminated terrain and material. The use of toxic chemical agents or biological agents may cause enemy activities which make the collection of information easier. For example, the use of persistent toxic chemicals may cause the enemy to vacate an area in which he has been well concealed.

ENEMY CAPABILITIES. The enemy's chemical and biological warfare capabilities and the effects of toxic chemical or biological agents on the area of operations are considered in analyses of the area of operations, intelligence estimates, and collection plans.

The surprise with which toxic chemical and biological agents can be used and the difficulties involved in immediate detection of such use, particularly verification of a biological attack, make indications of such use important in collection plans.

Counterintelligence plans should include measures to prevent the enemy from learning of any intentions of the friendly force to use toxic chemical or biological agents.

AREA OF OPERATIONS. Effective use of chemical and biological warfare requires information and intelligence of targets and predictions of the effects of the area characteristics on the use of toxic chemical and biological weapons. Scientifically, information is required of the effects of wind speed and direction, temperature, terrain, the degree of humidity, and the amount of precipitation on the use of toxic chemical or biological agents.

Chemical and biological contamination information is maintained and disseminated by the chemical officer under the supervision of the intelligence officer.

AIR DEFENSE

Air defense operations include all measures designed to destroy, nullify, or reduce the effectiveness of attack by hostile aircraft and aerodynamic or ballistic type missiles after they are airborne. Military operations on the earth's surface cannot be divorced from operations taking place in the air. Each side seeks to interfere with surface operations of his foe by aircraft and missile attack and air reconnaissance. The importance of effective air-defense is illustrated by the fact that the destructive power that could be delivered by 100,000 aircraft during World War II can now be delivered by one aircraft or missile armed with a nuclear warhead. At the same time, advances in air delivery systems have made the solution to the problem of effective air defense most difficult. Within the combat zone, the problem is very acute because of the very short warning time of an enemy air attack.

The rapidity of action in active air defense operations requires close integration of intelligence and operational activities. The provision of adequate, timely, reliable, and continuous intelligence is the backbone of air defense operations and is the function of the *air defense intelligence system*. The system consists of a series of integrated radar and communication networks including *early warning* and *surveillance* systems and acquisition and fire control radars. *Early warning networks* provide long-range warning of possible attack by aircraft and missiles. These networks are co-ordinated by air defense commanders. *Surveillance systems* are the joint responsibilities of regional and field army air defense commanders under the supervision of higher headquarters. Army air defense surveillance operations are coordinated by the local Army air defense commander. In the combat zone the early warning and surveillance systems are usually combined. Acquisition and fire control radars are used primarily to acquire specific targets and to control the fires of specific air defense units. These radars, while not an integral part of the air defense intelligence system, are netted with and augment the intelligence system. Acquisition and fire control radars, when not actively used in their primary function, may be used to fill gaps in the air defense intelligence system.

The intelligence officer, in support of air defense operations, provides intelligence of the enemy capability for attack by air or missile. He also integrates the air defense intelligence system into the overall plan for combat surveillance and ensures the timely exchange of information and intelligence between the air defense intelligence system and other collection agencies. Air defense operations are supported by counterintelligence measures such as passive air defense activities (including camouflage) and counter-sabotage measures.

CHAPTER 9

INFLUENCE OF MODERN WARFARE ON INTELLIGENCE OPERATIONS

Modern warfare is characterized by varying forms of possible war, possible use of nuclear weapons and extent of such use, and joint operations with other services or combined operations with allies. These conditions, except for use of nuclear weapons, have always been present to a degree. However, they are now of greater influence because of the power struggle between two major opposing coalitions, led by the United States and the Soviet Union, and the existence of the condition known as "situations short of war."

NUCLEAR WARFARE

The use of nuclear weapons greatly influence intelligence requirements. These requirements vary with the military operations that are possible under different scales of nuclear weapon use. The degree to which nuclear weapons are used affects the relationship between fire and maneuver. This in turn influences target acquisition activities and production of intelligence on avenues of approach. Similarly, the size of the area required for dispersion of units and installations is also affected with consequent influence on the production of intelligence of the area of operations.

INTERMEDIATE SCALE OF USE. When the extent of use of nuclear weapons is such that maneuver generally dominates tactical operations, the scale of use of nuclear weapons is called intermediate. Under these conditions, intelligence operations are primarily concerned with target acquisition and intelligence that influences maneuver. Without sufficient intelligence on targets, firepower cannot be used to meet effectively and possible courses of action are limited. Under this condition, combat forces also stress speed, dispersion, and battlefield mobility both on ground and in the air. Intelligence of air and ground routes are keys to selection of friendly courses of action and determination of enemy capabilities and vulnerabilities. This same intelligence indicates the area in which to concentrate target acquisition. Counterintelligence operations, in this situation, are concentrated on protection of nuclear delivery weapons and equipment and reduction of the enemy ability to locate targets. The enemy capabilities to deliver nuclear fires must also be determined in order to plan measures to reduce or destroy the effectiveness of these capabilities. This intelligence also enables the commander to judge better the degree of acceptable vulnerability and may be the deciding factor in selecting course of action and locating installations.

UNRESTRICTED USE. During unrestricted use of nuclear weapons, certain intelligence operations are stressed. As nuclear weapons use increases, firepower tends to predominate over maneuver. When this is the case, intelligence activities are more concerned with target acquisition and counterintelligence than on determination of the influence of the area on mobility. Large scale use of nuclear fires requires target acquisition activities that can produce timely results without risking the destruction of a disproportionate part of the command. Counterintelligence operations are increased to protect the command by denying the enemy target information.

VARYING FORMS OF WAR

Under all forms of war (situations short of war, limited war, general war), intelligence requirements are generally the same, but vary in importance with the particular form. For example, a theater commander always requires intelligence of the political aspects of his area because all major military decisions have political implications. However, to a division commander, political considerations are usually more important during situations short of war. Generally, under that form of war, requirements for intelligence of the political factor are very extensive.

SITUATIONS SHORT OF WAR. In situations short of war, intelligence that provides warning of outbreak of hostilities is of utmost importance. Commanders also require information and intelligence of all areas in the world where their forces may be committed. This information and intelligence must be provided as a matter of routine for units that may be committed on short notice. Once a mission is assigned, then *detailed* information and intelligence is required of the objective area with special emphasis on the political, social, and economic aspects. The information and intelligence are usually derived from current strategic intelligence produced by the military departments and other governmental agencies. Arrangements are also made to obtain intelligence from agencies within the area of operations and to develop all sources of information, particularly about guerrillas or dissident forces. Within the area of operations, intelligence is required on the background of the unrest, on dissident elements, on characteristics of the area, and on other factors which influence military action.

Counterintelligence operations are very important in situations short of war and start with receipt of the mission. Success may be endangered by enemy countermeasures if the friendly objectives become known in advance. Counterintelligence measures must overcome the handicap imposed by freedom of movement of civilians and news representatives. If time permits, cover and deception operations may be started. Within the objective area, counterintelligence operations provide for security of information, supplies, equipment, personnel, and installations. Lack of effective counterintelligence operations contributes to pilferage, blackmarket activity, diversion of supplies and arms to dissident forces, and propaganda discrediting the friendly force.

Intensive training of all individuals in security measures is important. Close contact with civilians and absence of combat frequently result in careless execution of individual security measures. Counterintelligence measures to provide security of planning operations require special attention. These measures must overcome the inability to impose censorship and other wartime controls, and must consider the effects of continued close consultations with local civilian officials and allies. Such close consultations pose a threat of information leaks. The demand for interpreters is often beyond the capabilities of the friendly force and is usually met by hiring local interpreters. Security checks of such personnel must be unusually thorough. Friendly police and security agencies can often assist with such checks.

LIMITED WAR. In limited war, intelligence operations are affected by the nature of the restrictions that make the war limited. When the restriction is a limitation on extent of nuclear weapon use, intelligence operations are influenced as discussed before. Other restrictions may be on the area of operations, limitation on targets, and on the use of weapons or means such as chemical and biological agents. Although certain weapons may be either restricted in their use or not used at all, intelligence operations must provide warning of the enemy suddenly disregarding the restraints and the conflict developing into general war. The extent of intelligence activities to determine whether the enemy will disregard restraints depends on the threat of the end of the existing restrictions. In any case, intelligence that provides warning of the extension of the conflict into general war is an urgent requirement.

GENERAL WAR. At the outbreak of a general war starting with a heavy exchange of large yield nuclear fires, emphasis is placed on maintaining the ability to collect information and producing intelligence which will warn of the start of enemy major ground tactical operations. When tactical operations are in progress, emphasis is placed on securing necessary intelligence to permit achieving superiority of fires and maintaining the security of the command.

COMPOSITION OF FRIENDLY FORCE

The composition of the friendly force is another major influence in the conduct of intelligence operations. At times, a headquarters may conduct intelligence operations normally performed by a higher headquarters. For example, in a small theater of operations a field army headquarters may be required to perform the intelligence operations normally conducted by a theater army headquarters; a reinforced division may be required to perform some of the intelligence operations normal to a field army. In such cases, augmentation with appropriate intelligence units and agencies is required.

COMBINED OPERATIONS. When the friendly force contains armed forces of other nations, liaison must be maintained with the intelligence agencies of all the participating armed forces. Subject to the policies established by a theater commander, certain intelligence operations may be a combined effort by all the nations making up the force. Combined efforts avoid duplication and ensure maximum dissemination of available intelligence. In working with intelligence agencies of other nations, care and tact are necessary in order to protect the security of specified types of information and still maintain cooperative relations. Information and intelligence to be disseminated only to US forces are kept to the minimum.

JOINT OPERATIONS. In joint operations with other services of the US armed forces, basic intelligence functions are unchanged. However, the force structure influences intelligence organization and procedures. Each Service component of the force assists the others in producing intelligence to the extent permitted by their own requirements and those of the joint or unified force commander. To do this, each component must know the intelligence requirements of the other components. The overall commander ensures that duplication of intelligence operations within the force is avoided by assignment of missions and responsibilities and the monitoring of operations. Assignment of missions should include responsibilities for collection and dissemination of information and intelligence and responsibilities for counterintelligence operations to include standard security measures.

The intelligence officer of the force plans the collection effort to provide the timely intelligence required by the commander. In assigning collection tasks, he considers the availability and capability of agencies to fulfill tasks, regardless of Service component. At the same time, each Service component also collects the intelligence information it needs and freely exchanges such information with the other Services. In producing intelligence, the force headquarters considers the enemy information as a whole and not as separate Army, Navy, or Air Force intelligence. Complete integration of all information is necessary in order to estimate the whole enemy situation.

In large joint or unified forces, the time lag in communications may make it desirable for the overall headquarters to perform intelligence functions normally performed by the individual Service departments in Washington, D. C. These functions could include publication of technical intelligence bulletins and intelligence of general orientation character and preparation and dissemination of other intelligence. Usefulness of intelligence should not be endangered because of delay in dissemination by the departments of the armed services concerned.

SUMMARY

In summary, it can be said that an insight into the influence of modern warfare on intelligence operations materially assists in the direction of intelligence operations. This insight and understanding is essential if timely and useful intelligence is to be provided to help solve the basic problems of the command and prevent surprise by the enemy.

CHAPTER 10

INTELLIGENCE RESPONSIBILITIES, ORGANIZATION AND TRAINING

Now that intelligence operations have been discussed, the responsibilities, organization, and training connected with these operations can be examined. To carry out intelligence operations successfully, a clear understanding of responsibilities for these operations is necessary or things will not get done. Further, an efficient organization is required to direct and supervise them. No intelligence officer is such a genius that he can do everything himself. Above all, the units and individuals involved require training.

RESPONSIBILITIES

THE COMMANDER. The commander is responsible for securing and using whatever intelligence he requires to accomplish his mission. He is also responsible for counterintelligence. The intelligence officer (director of security in logistical commands) is his principal assistant in this field. Although the commander relies heavily on the intelligence officer, the commander's responsibility is not reduced in any way.

Usually the adequacy of the intelligence that a commander has available is in direct proportion to his interest in intelligence and his use of it. If the commander bases his plans *only* on the capabilities of his own forces and map reconnaissance of the area, his chances of success are reduced. If the enemy has superiority in firepower, the commander who disregards intelligence will inevitably be defeated. To ensure that adequate intelligence is on hand when needed, the commander must be actively interested in the training and operations of his intelligence staff and agencies. Neglecting them in training periods and assigning them a disproportionate share of duties not connected with intelligence activities is laying the groundwork for battlefield failure. The intelligence officer who is kept busy by such duties as chairman of fund-raising

99

campaigns and club officer is not being trained to be a capable assistant in carrying out the commander's responsibilities for intelligence operations.

THE INTELLIGENCE OFFICER. The responsibilities of the intelligence officer have been discussed throughout the previous chapters. In summary, his responsibilities are:

Production of intelligence of the enemy, weather, terrain, and other characteristics of the area of operations;

Counterintelligence;

Intelligence and counterintelligence support of all combat and administrative support operations;

Intelligence training in coordination with the operations officer.

These are also peacetime responsibilities. Peacetime collection activities, for example, include the collection of maps and aerial photographs of the unit area and other areas of possible interest. All possible sources are used to collect information that may be needed by the unit. Sources that should not be neglected are local police, forest rangers, highway departments, local newspapers, and libraries. Weather information is important in peacetime and special local weather forecasts and climate summaries are often useful. These can be obtained from the local weather bureau as well as through military channels. The goal is to have the whole unit know that the intelligence section is a source of useful information and that if the information is not immediately available, it will be obtained.

Evaluation and interpretation are also carried on in peacetime. For example, the intelligence officer informs the commander and the staff of the effects of predicted weather conditions on what the unit is doing—whether it be training or movement of supplies. The intelligence officer should also periodically brief the commander and the staff on the various intelligence reports received from higher headquarters. Such briefings are one part of the responsibility of disseminating intelligence. The necessity for counterintelligence operations also exists in peacetime. Rules for protecting procedures, classified information, and equipment must be established and *supervised*. Above all, adequate files are maintained. An intelligence officer who acquires a lot of information but keeps it in his head and takes the information with him when he leaves is a failure as an intelligence officer and a staff officer. Without adequate files of background information, production of intelligence is handicapped.

The intelligence officer is not the only staff officer with intelligence and counterintelligence responsibilities. Almost everything that a unit does affects intelligence and counterintelligence activities. Intelligence operations are not separate and distinct functions apart from other military operations. No intelligence officer can work in a world of his own. His activities are interrelated with those supervised by other staff officers. Figure 19 shows the major activities of an intelligence officer and the related activities of other staff officers.

STAFF ORGANIZATION

The staff organization used by the intelligence officer depends on the mission of the command, the scope of expected intelligence activities, the personnel available, and his preferences and those of the commander. Usually a functional organization is used with specific responsibilities assigned to major subdivisions. In wartime, the staff organization must be capable of continuous 24-hour operation, meeting peak work loads, and displacing without disruption of operations. The intelligence sections at division, corps, and field army headquarters are usually organized with *Operations, G2 Air, Counterintelligence,* and *Administrative* Branches. Other branches are added as required. Division, corps, and field army headquarters intelligence sections are generally organized in the same manner but with minor modifications due to variations in scope of intelligence activities. For example, the field army intelligence staff operations branch has an analysis selection because of added responsibilities for production of strategic intelligence and intelligence on enemy air, missile, and nuclear capabilities.

The army group headquarters intelligence section generally parallels the corps and field army intelligence section in organization. However, branches are smaller because the army group delegates to field armies territorial responsibilities and control of clandestine operations and the army group interrogates few prisoners of war. The intelligence section organization of the army

Activity	G2	G3	G1	G4	G5	Special staff officers
1. Collection of information. a. Ground reconnaissance.	Develops plans and coordinates ground reconnaissance of the command.	Designates combat units for reconnaissance. Plans reconnaissance in force. Coordinates ground reconnaissance with combat patrols and with other combat operations including fires. (G3 air coordinates air-to-surface fires in area of reconnaissance.)	Maintains personnel strength of reconnaissance units.		Provides assistance, such as guides, from local population for reconnaissance units. Provides information from local population to include line crossers, refugees, etc.	Armor—recommends employment of armor units for reconnaissance. Arty—provides supporting and interdiction fires. Provides forward observer personnel. Coordinates surface-to-surface fires in area of reconnaissance. Avn—assists in transporting, controlling, and supplying ground recon elements. CmI—provides information on contaminated areas. Engr—performs ground reconnaissance and secures and provides terrain data and terrain studies. PM—provides information on refugees, civilian interesses, local population, guerrilla activities, and terrain. Sig—provides communications and ground photography as required. Trans—provides transportation as required.
b. Use of air reconnaissance (Army aviation).	Originates requests and consolidates and screens requests from other staff elements, agencies, or units. Assigns missions. Disseminates results of reconnaissance. Coordinates use of air reconnaissance with other collection activities.	Coordinates with other operational air missions.	Examine availability of specialists personnel to include observers.			Arty—coordinates suppression of artillery fires in area of reconnaissance, target marking, and flak suppression fires, as required. Avn—assigns missions. Coordinates priorities on use of Army aviation. Furnishes technical advice on use of Army aviation. Sig—reproduces and distributes airphotos. Coordinates in establishing priorities for photographic support.
c. Use of air reconnaissance supporting services).	Originate requests for air reconnaissance. Consolidates and screens requests from other staff elements, agencies, and units. Disseminates results of reconnaissance.	Shares use of air request and information nets and spot report receivers. Coordinates with offensive air missions.				Avn—furnishes Army aviation for photo delivery. Coordinates with Army aviation operations. Sig—delivers airphotos. Engr—uses photos to obtain and produce terrain intelligence.
d. Surveillance.	Plans for systematic watch of the battle area. Assigns missions. Coordinates all surveillance activities.	Designates units for conduct of surveillance over enemy. Furnishes information on locations of own forces and operation plans. Designates required target characteristics information.	Ensures availability of specialist personnel.	Coordinates regulated equipment requirements.		Avn—provides Army aviation for airborne surveillance devices. Arty—requests information on physical characteristics of targets acquired for target analysis. Informs G2 of combat surveillance information received from artillery and other sources.
e. Target acquisition.	Plans target acquisition in coordination with G3. Assigns collection missions and coordinates collection of target information. Designates potential targets and disseminates this information to the staff.	Determines characteristics and target development requirements. Evaluates potential targets developed by G2; makes general target analyses.			Furnishes information from local population to include line crossers, refugees, etc. Evaluates civil aspects of potential targets developed by G2.	Avn—provides Army aviation for photography and visual delivery services. Arty—makes detailed target analyses and furnishes target information.
f. Prediction of fallout and radiological monitoring and survey.						
g. Technical intelligence.	Coordinates activities of technical intelligence detachment. Uses technical intelligence in estimates and studies. Disseminates technical intelligence to appropriate agencies.	Designates combat units for technical intelligence support, including guards. Plans for technical intelligence targets. Coordinates use of enemy weapons and equipment. Receives and requests technical intelligence that may affect operations.	Receives technical intelligence that may affect personnel activities.	Assists in evacuation of technical intelligence material. Coordinates use of enemy material. Receives and requests technical intelligence that may affect logistical activities.	Advises on use of local agencies for guarding technical intelligence material. Plans for technical intelligence targets. Receives and requests technical intelligence that may affect civil activities to include use of enemy material.	All—furnish and receive information of enemy troops, materiel, supply, installations, training, tactics, and capabilities in their respective areas of interest. Assist in evaluating information. ASA—provides G2 with intelligence requirements of materiel of interest to USASA. Arty—requests technical intelligence of target characteristics.

Activity					
4. Signal intelligence (SIGINT).	Develop SIGINT requirements. Produces and disseminates signal intelligence.				ASA—advises G2 on capabilities and limitations of USAS units and recommends their employment.
2. Production of intelligence and information.					
a. Preparation and analyses of area of operations.	Prepares and disseminates analyses of area of operations.	The analysis of area of operations is used by all staff officers for estimation of effect of terrain on activities with which they are concerned.		Furnishes and receives information of population, government, economy and institutions.	Acty—furnishes meteorological information. Engr—furnishes terrain and environmental studies and information on obstacles.
b. Preparation of intelligence estimates.	Prepares and disseminates intelligence estimates.	The intelligence estimate is used by all staff officers for estimation of the effect on activities with which they are concerned.			
c. Planning for and distribution of maps and map substitutes (less supplies).	Supervises procurement, distribution, and storage. Prescribes allowances, scales, and types (in coordination with G3).	Projects units boundaries for planned operations and on this basis recommends type, scales, and distribution.	Provides materials for fabrication of map substitutes. Provides storage and transportation.	Makes available local resources for special requirements.	Engr—advises on availability. Determines specific requirements, Requisitions, stores, and issues. Fabricates map substitutes.
3. Direction of the collection effort. Development of EEI (Essential elements of information)	Recommends EEI to the commander based on determination of information and intelligence requirements and recommendations of other staff officers. Disseminates approved EEI.	Advises on tentative courses of action and operation plan. Recommends to G2 EEI on enemy capability, vulnerabilities, and characteristics of area of operations having major effect on accomplishment of the mission.	Recommends to G2 EEI on enemy capabilities and characteristics of area of operations having major effect on personnel activities.	Recommends to G2 EEI on enemy capabilities and characteristics of area of operations having major effect on logistical activities.	Cml—recommends EEI pertaining to CB operations. Engr—recommends EEI pertaining to terrain. Acty—recommends EEI pertaining to potential targets. Sig—recommends EEI pertaining to electronic warfare. ASA—recommends EEI pertaining to communications and electronic intelligence.
4. Counterintelligence. Planning counterintelligence measures.	Prepares counterintelligence estimates. Plans and supervises implementation of counterintelligence measures to support all operations.	Ensures support of operations. Determines effect on operations to minimize interference. Designates forces, area, equipment, and operations (including training) requiring priority measures. Countercontaminance. Concealment and cover.	Coordinates personnel activities such as uniform, insignia, leave policies, and morale activities. Plans special handling of POWs. Determines effect on personnel activities.	Determines effect on logistical activities. Designates area of material requiring priority measures.	Implements civil security and censorship measures. Provides civilian law enforcement agencies. Assists in plans for detection of enemy agents, line crossers, subversive personnel, etc. Implements port, frontier, and travel security measures.	All—plans security of their respective installations and activities. Avn—provides air observation of effectiveness of camouflage and concealment. Cml—provides screening agents. Engr—advises on camouflage. Sig and ASA—advises on communications and electronic security. PM—provides control of personnel traffic circulation. Protects selected equipment and installations. IG—for the control of security aspects of command area releases. Plans for control of accredited press media representatives.
5. Training. Training of units in intelligence.	Trains own section. Supervises intelligence training of all subordinate units. Establishes unit schools. Prepares intelligence training programs. Establishes requirements for intelligence training material. Assists subordinate units.	Approves intelligence training program of instruction. Allocates time and facilities in unit training program. Integrates with other training. Coordinates division intelligence schools. Coordinates on training aids. Keeps informed on status of intelligence training in units.		Arrange fabrication of special intelligence training aids.	Supervises intelligence training of CA units.	All—supervise intelligence training of their respective personnel and units.

Figure 19. Relationships in selected intelligence activities.

group headquarters must provide for special information security measures when the army group is a combined headquarters controlling the forces of other nations. Usually, this is done by providing a US documents control element.

The theater army logistical command headquarters intelligence staff organization is part of the staff organization that is also responsible for rear area security and rear area damage control. The whole organization is under a *director of security*. The organization of the intelligence division of the directorate of security reflects the mission of the command—administrative support and territorial responsibilities. In medium and small logistical command headquarters, the staff organizations for intelligence and for rear area security and rear area damage control are usually further combined with the staff organization responsible for plans and operations under a *director of security, plans and operations*. The intelligence staff organization of this directorate is about the same as that of the theater army logistical command except it is smaller because of the reduced scope of activities, smaller force supported and smaller area of responsibility.

The theater army headquarters intelligence division is organized to *supervise* and *coordinate* intelligence aspects of the operational, administrative, and territorial responsibilities which have been delegated to subordinate elements. Appendix XXIII shows the functional organization of intelligence staffs at division, corps, field army, theater army logistical command, and theater army headquarters.

TRAINING

The intelligence training of a unit consists of two tasks—training of the personnel of intelligence staff sections and the intelligence training of all other personnel. Intelligence training can become confused unless the responsibilities of these two tasks are clearly understood by all involved with planning and supervising training. The intelligence officer is responsible for the training of his own intelligence section. The operations officer is responsible for the general conduct, planning, and supervision of *all* training within a unit. The intelligence officer *assists* the operations officer by staff supervision—not direction—of all intelligence training within the command. Commanders are responsible for the intelligence training of their units and all staff officers are responsible for the intelligence training of their staff sections.

The intelligence officer, in coordination with the operations officer, prepares the unit intelligence training program, conducts intelligence schools, supervises intelligence training, conducts tests, and assists subordinate units in obtaining training aids and qualified instructors. He recommends to the operations officer the amount of time needed for intelligence training and requirements for facilities, training aids, and instructors. Close coordination by the intelligence officer with the other members of the staff and subordinate commanders helps insure that intelligence training is integrated with other training.

CENTRALIZED SCHOOL. A time-proven method for the *initial* training of intelligence staff sections is a centralized school— preferably conducted by a division headquarters. All personnel assigned to an intelligence staff section within the division should attend this school. In addition, units not authorized an intelligence section should send at least one officer and one or more enlisted men. Upon completion of this school, subordinate units should conduct their own intelligence schools to train other personnel of their units using personnel who attended the division school as instructors. A system of intelligence schools within the command helps to establish standard practices.

COMMAND POST EXERCISES. Centralized schooling of intelligence staff personnel should be followed by command post exercises (CPX). These exercises may vary from a map maneuver held in one room to elaborate exercises in which all the intelligence section and communications facilities are actually used. These exercises are built around the use of previously prepared messages requiring action by the players. These exercises are excellent training for field operations because they provide an opportunity for intelligence sections to practice their duties in the field as closely as possible short of actually going into the field.

This type of training is possible under any conditions of housing, equipment, availability of personnel, or state of training.

Once started, these exercises need not run continuously but may be conducted during a part of each day and stopped at any time for a critique. In its simplest form, this type of exercise requires only intelligence personnel and does not interfere with other training. It also is an excellent way to cross-train within an intelligence section to prepare personnel to perform the duties of others in case of need.

INTEGRATION WITH OTHER TRAINING. The training of intelligence section personnel does not end with the completion of command post exercises. Intelligence training is perfected by integration with other training and on-the-job training. If personnel of an intelligence section cannot be fully utilized during certain training periods, they should be made available to help other staff sections which have need for their special skills. For example, the draftsman who keeps the enemy situation map is training for his job when he prepares a training area sketch for the G3 or a special chart for the G4.

INTELLIGENCE TRAINING FOR ALL PERSONNEL. The intelligence training for all other personnel should be integrated with other training except for specialized subjects and orientation. As far as practicable, intelligence training for the command as a whole should not be conducted as a separate activity distinct from other training. This type of intelligence training should emphasize *collection and reporting of information and security of military information.* This training should include sources of information with which any individual may come in contact. Particularly, it should cover handling of prisoners of war, enemy dead, captured documents and equipment, and instruction on *how* and *when* and to *whom* information is reported. Speed in collection and reporting of information and the extension of collection activities to the depth of the area of influence of the unit should be emphasized. Training in security of military information should include—at the minimum—instruction in the handling of classified documents, the danger of loose talk, security requirements in the use of radios and telephones, the information that can be given if captured, and enemy methods of interrogating prisoners of war.

MANEUVERS. Intelligence play in maneuvers and exercises

should furnish realistic training in every aspect of combat intelligence, from the collection of information to the production of intelligence. Units should be provided with the intelligence facilities and means normally required during combat operations and realistic situations to use these facilities and equipment. The use of a maneuver enemy, such as Aggressor, improves realism and helps make commanders, staffs, and troops conscious of the enemy as a real opposing force. Where possible, intelligence activities in maneuvers and exercises should include air and ground reconnaissance, use of surveillance devices, safeguarding military information, camouflage and camouflage discipline, restrictions on the use of communications, radiological monitoring reporting of nuclear bursts, and the requisition and distribution of maps. By the use of imagination and ingenuity, the intelligence officer can make every field exercise an interesting and profitable exercise in intelligence operations.

APPENDIX I

THE NATIONAL INTELLIGENCE ORGANIZATION

The *National Intelligence Organization* is considered to consist of all the agencies and departments of the Federal Government which have intelligence interests or responsibilities. It is generally called a national intelligence organization because the intelligence produced by all the components is brought together for the use of the National Security Council, which is the highest policy advisory board to the President.

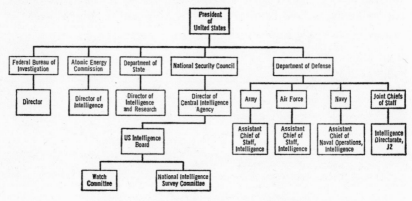

Figure 20. National intelligence organization.

The *National Security Council,* established in 1947, is directly under the President. The Council establishes the policies which guide and coordinate the national intelligence effort, creates committees for specific intelligence functions, and assigns responsibilities to the various components of the national intelligence organization for specific duties in certain fields of intelligence.

The *Central Intelligence Agency* (CIA), also established in 1947, is directly under the National Security Council and has a Director and Deputy Director appointed by the President. The CIA coordinates the intelligence activities of the other intelligence departments and agencies. It advises the National Security Council on these activities as related to national security, recommends and evaluates intelligence on national security, and disseminates such intelligence within the government.

The *United States Intelligence Board* is the major coordinating agency of the national intelligence organization. It includes members from the Central Intelligence Agency, the Army, Navy, Air Force, Federal Bureau of Investigation, and the Atomic Energy Commission. The Director of Central Intelligence is the chairman of the board.

Within the State Department, the *Director of Intelligence and Research* develops and carries out the Department of State foreign intelligence program. He provides the intelligence support needed by the Secretary of State as a member of the National Security Council and advisor to the President on foreign policy. The Directory of Intelligence and Research also provides intelligence to the policy officers of the Department of State and maintains liaison with other governmental intelligence organizations.

Within the Department of Defense each of the military departments, Army, Navy, and Air Force, maintains an intelligence organization to satisfy their special requirements. The Department of the Army, Navy, and the Air Force each has an *Assistant Chief of Staff* who is responsible for planning and supervising departmental activities including the collection of information abroad by military attaches. In addition, the Joint Chiefs of Staff have their own intelligence organization, known as the *J2 Intelligence Directorate*. This Directorate is not an information collection agency, but relies on information and intelligence produced by the CIA, the military departments, and other agencies. This information and intelligence is processed for use by the Joint Chiefs of Staff, the Joint Staff, and the Secretary of Defense.

The principal governmental body for the coordination and exchange of information on internal security is the *Interdepartmental Intelligence Conference*. This Conference, composed of a member from the FBI, the Army, Navy, and the Air Force, coordinates the investigation of all domestic espionage, counter-espionage sabotage, subversion, and related internal security matters.

The division of responsibility for collecting information required for national intelligence is based on three major geographical and political areas. These three areas are the United States, foreign nations where no United States military forces are stationed, and foreign nations under their own control in which United States military forces are stationed.

Within the United States, responsibility for collecting intelligence information is based on the principle of the supremacy of civil authority over the military. Therefore, the responsibilities for intelligence operations affecting the rights and prerogatives of civilians are assigned to a civilian agency of the executive branch of the government—the *Federal Bureau of Investigation*. However, only military commanders conduct military intelligence activities within their own forces.

Intelligence collection activities in areas in which there are no United States military forces stationed are considered as acts unfriendly to the countries concerned. An exception is the collection of information by military attaches in accordance with established diplomatic practices.

In foreign areas where United States military forces are stationed, they are normally given the right by treaty or agreement to conduct, as needed for their own security, intelligence activities within their own forces and in the immediate surrounding area. This does not include collecting information about the nation in which they are stationed. This information is gathered by military attaches in keeping with normal diplomatic procedures.

Naturally, in time of war, military commanders coordinate and control all intelligence activities in their areas.

APPENDIX II

ORDER OF BATTLE INTELLIGENCE FACTORS

UNIT IDENTIFICATION

The unit identification factor is the complete designation of a specific unit, containing a number, a branch of service and a specified size, such as a regiment or a division. Some foreign units lack numerical and branch of service elements in their designation, having instead only a special name. By identifying individual enemy units, the composition of the total enemy force is eventually established. Unit identification answers the commander's question: "Who is opposing me?" Identification of a unit is the basis for developing the remaining order of battle factors.

DISPOSITION

The disposition factor is the location, tactical deployment, and the movement of enemy units. Disposition includes the location of the headquarters of each identified unit and the deployment of all its troops. The disposition factor answers the commander's question: "Where are the enemy units?" To make correct estimates the commander and the staff must know how enemy units are deployed. This knowledge also helps indicate the relative probability of adoption of enemy capabilities. The study of dispositions, coupled with an analysis of terrain, supports logical conclusions as to individual unit boundaries. Movement of units is an important aspect of disposition. A moving unit is capable of a number of different actions such as attack, reinforcement of another unit, replacement of another unit, or other missions.

STRENGTH

The strength factor includes the total number of enemy personnel and equipment (armored vehicles, artillery, etc.) together with the amount of administrative support. Strength is expressed by stating either the estimated personnel strength of the enemy

111

force, or the number of battalions of infantry, artillery, and armor. These three combat arms can be further defined as mechanized or motorized infantry, medium or heavy tanks, missile units, and calibers of artillery. The factor of strength answers the commander's question: "How strong is the enemy?" Intelligence estimates, in part, are based on knowledge of enemy strength. Determining enemy strength accurately is extremely difficult.

ORGANIZATION

The organization factor includes the types of units in the enemy forces and the relationship of units within the command structure. Types of units refer to branches of service such as infantry, tank, airborne, etc. The organization of units of each type must be established. In establishing the command structure of a unit, the numerical designations both of its subordinate components and its parent unit are determined.

When contact with the enemy is made, knowledge of enemy organization becomes very important. If an enemy motorized rifle regiment is identified, the order of battle analyst immediately attempts to determine which other rifle regiments are present and their locations. He knows what to look for as to number, types, and sizes of units organic to an enemy division, as well as the probable composition of the regiment contacted. Knowledge of organization leads to the development of other factors on the uncontacted components of the enemy force. At times, enemy units which have an unorthodox organization will be identified. Failure to learn the organization of such an enemy unit places friendly forces at a disadvantage.

TACTICS

The tactics factor refers to the manner in which the enemy employs his units. Order of battle intelligence establishes the general tactics of different types of enemy units, the tactics used in special operations (amphibious operations, airborne assaults, river crossings, etc.) and the tactics used by individual units, when these tactics are peculiar to these units or indicate their possible future action.

Knowledge of enemy tactics is extremely important. Enemy

units can logically be expected to perform according to certain patterns within the framework of general tactics. There are patterns for the employment of infantry, armor, and artillery in both the offense and the defense. The enemy's tactical doctrine indicates courses of action in most special operations. Furthermore, individual enemy units are usually trained as specialist units for certain operations such as mountain warfare, desert warfare, arctic warfare, etc. The knowledge of how the enemy is trained to act in general and special situations and a knowledge of the specialties in which individual units have been trained can be of a great advantage.

PERSONALITIES

The personality factor refers to the characteristics and attributes of enemy individuals. Personality data on key command and high-level staff personnel are important to the friendly forces. In gathering this information, it is important to identify names with positions, and vice versa. Other information such as the individual's rank, date of rank, branch of service, personal traits and characteristics, civilian and military schooling, and combat record make a composite and often very enlightening picture of the individual. This knowledge can possibly lead to identification of an enemy unit. The name of a key member of an enemy unit may also tentatively identify that unit. The personal traits and the general ability of enemy military personnel have a direct bearing on the combat efficiency and tactics of their units.

COMBAT EFFICIENCY

Combat efficiency is the degree of effectiveness of an enemy unit in combat. Characteristics, qualities, and circumstances which affect a unit's combat efficiency include: strength in personnel, weapons, and equipment; length of time in combat; traditions and past performance; personality traits of the commander; geographical area, morale, and discipline; and status of training and administrative support. A commander operates differently against an enemy unit known to be of poor fighting quality than against a unit having an excellent combat reputation. When all the characteristics, qualities, and circumstances which affect combat efficiency are considered, this factor gains increased importance.

UNIT HISTORY

Unit history is a record of past performance of a unit. It includes the time and manner of activation of the unit, the unit's components, past and present parent units, combat record, places where the unit has trained, types of training, the names of past and present commanders, and a list of code names and numbers assigned the unit. The past performance of a unit often indicates its current combat efficiency. The knowledge of what an enemy unit has done in the past, where that unit has been, and the type of troops assigned to the unit helps provide information for establishing other order of battle factors about the unit.

ORDER OF BATTLE INFORMATION

The amount of detail of order of battle information kept at each headquarters varies with the size of the unit. However, regardless of the unit size, the order of battle intelligence effort covers all enemy forces to the front and flanks of the unit and those enemy units in reserve which may affect the friendly forces. To make recording and collating of order of battle information easier, various mechanical devices have been developed. One successful method uses the equipment of machine records units. Use of such equipment is generally not practical below field army headquarters. However, use of such equipment at field army headquarters makes complete order of battle information more readily available in subordinate units.

APPENDIX III

TECHNICAL INTELLIGENCE

Technical intelligence detachments collect, identify, and examine all captured enemy items and make preliminary tests on their capabilities, limitations, use, and effectiveness. They escort or arrange for the evacuation of selected enemy materiel and recommend disposition of materiel having no intelligence value. They also prepare questionnaires for prisoner-of-war interrogation and instruct troops on recognition characteristics, use, maintenance of enemy materiel, and interchangeability of our own and Allied materiel. They also evaluate effectiveness of our own and Allied weapons and ammunition against enemy materiel and recommend countermeasures. In the field of enemy scientific and technical achievements in research, development, production, and storage, technical intelligence detachments make preliminary analyses to determine what further detailed analyses should be made.

Within a division, capture of a new item or one of special interest is reported to the unit intelligence officer who informs the next higher headquarters. The division G2 notifies the appropriate technical intelligence detachment if one is operating in the area. If not, he notifies the next higher headquarters. The first objective after capture of enemy materiel is to obtain information of immediate value to combat forces—particularly recognition characteristics, capabilities, limitations, and countermeasures. This information is obtained mainly from examination of the captured materiel and additional information from captured documents and interrogations. Detailed field examination is usually made at a technical service installation. The item is then evacuated, if appropriate, to the zone of interior. All preliminary and final reports of examination are also sent to the appropriate intelligence officer.

Within Army divisions, captured materiel is collected by combat units. The materiel is evacuated either to the division salvage collecting point or to the appropriate technical service installation. Further evacuation is the responsibility of the field army technical services. Heavy or fragile enemy materiel in forward areas is inspected in place by technical intelligence detachments *(TID's)* in order to determine emplacement techniques, damage caused by our weapons, and intelligence value. Heavy materiel of no intelligence value is left in place for salvage or recovery in accordance with theater standing operating procedures.

Technical intelligence is disseminated by all headquarters. The Departments of the Army, Navy, and Air Force publish material on the equipment and armament of foreign forces. Within the theater of operations, dissemination of technical intelligence is normally confined to items of immediate concern to troops and theater agencies. For example, extracts of a captured enemy manual on a new antitank gun would be disseminated, but information about enemy developments in a specialized field of science would not.

APPENDIX IV

SOURCES OF INFORMATION

PRISONERS OF WAR

Prisoners of war are valuable sources of information, particularly of the immediate battle area and of the effects of our psychological warfare operations. Maximum information is obtained through skillful handling of prisoners of war from the time of capture until interrogation is completed. Interrogation personnel are carefully briefed on the information desired and provided with aids such as maps and aerial photos.

INTERROGATION. Immediately upon capture, prisoners, particularly those wounded, are likely to be suffering from shock and lowered morale, which makes interrogation easier. Rapid evacuation reduces the delay between the time of capture and interrogation by trained prisoner of war (IPW) interrogators. Evacuation from division and larger units is a responsibility of military police. Evacuation of prisoners of war to the division collecting point is the responsibility of combat troops. As an aid to interrogation, prisoners are segregated by rank whenever possible. Access to prisoners of war for intelligence purposes takes priority over evacuation except when prohibited by the Geneva Convention.

Prisoners of war are briefly interrogated at company, battle group, and combat command level for information of immediate tactical value. Detailed interrogation of selected prisoners of war takes place at division and field army. All prisoners are screened during the evacuation process and some are designated for further interrogation at higher headquarters and at camps behind the combat zone.

According to their intelligence value, prisoners of war may be divided for convenience into the following categories:

Category A. Prisoners of war whose broad or specific knowl-

117

edge of the enemy war effort requires immediate interrogation by specially qualified interrogators of the highest headquarters in the theater.

Category B. Prisoners of war with enough information about the enemy on any subject of intelligence value, in addition to information of tactical value, to warrant a second interrogation.

Category C. Prisoners of war with only information of immediate tactical value and do not warrant a second interrogation.

Category D. Prisoners of war of no intelligence value.

From a division prisoner of war collecting point, prisoners are evacuated by field army military police to field army prisoner of war cages. From there, prisoners are evacuated to camps in the communications zone and then if possible to the zone of the interior. Corps may interrogate selected prisoners at division collecting points using corps interrogators. Army group may do the same at field army prisoner of war cages. Exceptionally, corps and army group may interrogate selected prisoners at cages in the vicinity of their own headquarters. In such cases, corps and army group evacuate and hold such prisoners.

Procedures for interrogation of Army captured prisoners of war by other services and Allied forces are prescribed by the theater headquarters. Prisoner of war interrogation personnel of other Services and Allied forces may be attached to Army units for interrogation operations. The theater headquarters may establish a Joint Services Detailed Interrogation Center (JSDIC). The JSDIC is a highly specialized unit, staffed by interrogators from all services, to permit exploitation of military technical, psychological, political, economic, and other areas of information. Usually, only Category A prisoners of war are interrogated at JSDIC.

CIVILIANS

Civilians who have been within enemy controlled areas may be valuable sources of information about terrain and may also have knowledge of enemy installations and activities. Enemy civilians in recently captured areas often give information readily in consideration of their own self-interest. Generally, the longer the delay in questioning civilians, the less valid is the information obtained. Civilians from enemy controlled areas are carefully screened in order to detect line crossers and stay-behind enemy agents.

Civilian sources may also provide current information on matters such as terrain, climate, economics, sociology, psychology, and local resources. Law enforcement agencies may provide information on such matters as guerrilla and similar forces, line crossers, and stay-behind elements. In situations short of war, local civilians are particularly valuable sources for information of immediate areas of operation for divisions and smaller units. Actively hostile civilians normally are collected by combat units and are evacuated through prisoner of war channels. Civilians who are hostile but who do not carry arms and do not physically resist the friendly forces *are not* considered prisoners of war and are transferred to civil affairs control for disposition. The first positive establishment of civilian status is usually at battle group level prisoner-of-war collecting points. Identified civilians are screened for security suspects by personnel of the supporting military intelligence unit security section. Security section personnel may be augmented by civil police officials made available through the civil affairs officer.

RECOVERED MILITARY PERSONNEL

Recovered military personnel are sources of information of the area of operations and enemy dispositions and activities. Escapers and evaders are sources of information of successful evasion techniques. Interrogation of recovered military personnel is conducted as prescribed by the theater headquarters. Within these limits, interrogation at division level is usually limited to getting information of immediate tactical use. Recovered military personnel are evacuated as prescribed by the theater headquarters.

CAPTURED DOCUMENTS

Captured documents furnish information which is generally reliable. However, enemy plans may be based on false assumptions or may have been changed. Documents may also contain enemy propaganda, or may have been planted by the enemy to be captured and cause confusion and deception. Documents from a prisoner of war are evacuated with the prisoner, in custody of a guard, so that the prisoner can be questioned on the content of the documents. Documents from other sources are usually forwarded through intelligence channels. Small units inspect captured documents quickly for information of immediate tactical value and then promptly forward them to the intelligence officer of the next higher headquarters. Maximum collection of enemy documents is ensured by proper training of small units and individuals.

All documents, after a brief examination, are classified into three groups, by division and higher headquarters as follows:

"A" Documents. These are documents of *immediate tactical value.* Information from "A" documents is transmitted to higher headquarters and affected adjacent units as soon as possible. Category "A" documents are retained within the theater, and are available to any authorized agency. "A" documents which also contain strategic intelligence are handled as "B" documents after the needs of the theater have been met.

"B" Documents. These are documents of *strategic intelligence value.* After final examination at theater headquarters, these documents are forwarded to headquarters in the zone of the interior.

"C" Documents. These are documents of no military or strategic intelligence value. These are retained within the theater, to be disposed in accordance with theater instructions.

CAPTURED MATERIEL

Captured materiel may at times have immediate intelligence value by contributing to target information, order of battle intelligence, and development of enemy capabilities and vulnerabilities. The production of technical intelligence is assisted by a continuous collection and exploitation effort by both combat troops and the Technical Services. See appendix III.

ENEMY SIGNAL COMMUNICATIONS AND OTHER ELECTROMAGNETIC EMISSIONS

These are valuable sources of information of enemy plans and orders, unit identifications and locations, locations of fire control and surveillance devices, and similar data. Exploitation of these sources extends the depth of intelligence operations and contributes to target acquisition.

DUDS AND MISSILE AND SHELL FRAGMENTS

These are sources of information on the type and caliber of enemy supporting weapons. This information helps in order of battle intelligence and in the determination of enemy capabilities and vulnerabilities. Crater analysis helps in target acquisition by leading to the locations of enemy weapons. Examination of areas contaminated by toxic chemical and biological agents helps identify the agents used, develop countermeasures, and evaluate enemy capabilities. Information of areas contaminated by residual nuclear radiation is required in determining use of terrain and for troop safety.

SHELL REPORTS

Shell reports are made by the units fired upon. Reports of enemy use of toxic chemical or biological agents are made by all commands having such knowledge. The use of a standard form for such reports helps ensure that all required information is forwarded. A standard "Standard Shelling, Mortaring, Bombing, and Toxic Report" is given in appendix VIII.

NUCLEAR BURSTS

Information of nuclear bursts is required for predicting fallout and estimating effects on enemy capabilities. The information required includes time of burst, ground zero, height of burst, yield, cloud dimensions, and observed effects. All units observing a nuclear strike report such information. Appendix VIII gives a Nuclear Burst Report form.

PHOTOGRAPHS

Ground and aerial photographs are excellent sources of detailed information of terrain, for damage assessment, and of enemy activities, particularly fortifications, weapons positions, organization of tactical locations, movements, and location and extent of assembly areas. Ground photography for intelligence purposes includes panoramic views, large-scale coverage of specific objects and terrain features, flash recordings, and repetitive photographs for comparative purposes. A special type of coverage is by comparative motion picture with individual frames used as still frames rather than as a motion picture sequence. Color and infrared photography provides additional detail and helps detect camouflage.

Panoramic photos are taken from a dominant terrain feature and usually comprise a series of overlapping photographs. In addition to providing information of the area, they are useful as supplements to maps and air-photos in coordinating observation plans, planning ground reconnaissance activities, coordinating fires, and orienting personnel. Within the Army, ground photography is usually performed by Signal Corps units at division and higher headquarters.

MAPS

Maps are the principal source of information of terrain. The accuracy of a map depends on the data used in their preparation. Maps are supplemented by aerial or ground photographs, sketches, visual observation, trig lists, gazeteers and other information. *Trig lists* contain the exact location and elevation of benchmarks and other survey points, together with a complete description of their characteristics. Trig lists are of particular value to artillery units and in orienting certain surveillance devices.

WEATHER INFORMATION

Much of the field army's weather information is furnished by the Air Weather Service (AWS) of the Air Force. The Army satisfies its own weather information requirements for ballistic-meteorological data. Artillery meteorological sections can make winds-aloft observations and determine upper air pressure, temperature, and humidity. Chemical units collect information of surface winds, temperature, and humidity. Army aviators report weather conditions within their area of flight operations. All units can collect weather information by observation and, if required, may be equipped with instruments for collecting additional weather data.

AWS detachments maintain tactical weather stations at field army, corps, and divisions. These detachments maintain continuous watch over weather conditions in the area of the units served, advise commanders and staff officers of significant changes and developments in the weather situation, and produce or secure forecasts, reports of current weather, weather summaries, and climatological information.

OTHER SOURCES OF INFORMATION

These include informers, intelligence reports and studies prepared by higher, lower, and adjacent units, and reference materials prepared by the Office of the Assistant Chief of Staff for Intelligence, Department of the Army, and other Armed Services and governmental agencies.

APPENDIX V

FIELD ARMY MILITARY INTELLIGENCE ORGANIZATION

WITHIN THE ARMY

The *military intelligence battalion, field army,* assists the field army G2 in intelligence and counterintelligence operations and furnishes detachments to support corps and divisions. The battalion is completely self-supporting. When elements are attached to subordinate units of the field army, the military intelligence battalion retains administrative control of personnel actions, technical proficiency, training, certain technical support, and technical and policy guidance.

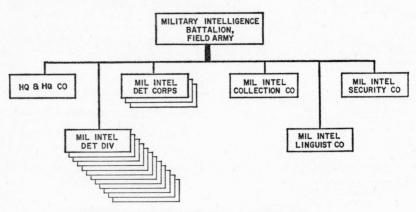

Figure 21. Military intelligence battalion, field army.

Certain elements of the battalion *headquarters company* are incorporated into the field army G2 section. Other elements execute missions assigned by the field army G2. The field army G2 may delegate to the military intelligence battalion operational control of specified military intelligence units that operate at the field army level.

The *military intelligence linguist company* provides the field

124

army G2 with specialized assistance in prisoner of war interrogation, translation of enemy documents, and interpretation and translation of the language spoken in the field army's area of operations.

The *interrogation of prisoner of war (IPW) platoon,* at full strength, can interrogate at three field army prisoner of war cages. At reduced strength the platoon can support one cage on a limited basis.

The functions of the *document translator platoon* are self-explanatory. The personnel of this unit are translators and not intelligence analysts.

The *interpreter/translator platoon* performs functions dealing with the language spoken in the area of operations of the field army. This platoon does not constitute an administrative interpreter pool for the field army headquarters. The platoon interprets or translates for other operational elements of the military intelligence battalion, interrogates civilians for information of intelligence value, and translates documents originating with Allied or friendly military elements. The platoon has a limited capability for temporary emergency augmentation of military intelligence detachments at corps and divisions.

The *security company* (formerly known as Counter Intelligence Corps Detachment) provides the field army G2 with the operational means to fulfill counterintelligence responsibilities. This company operates and controls teams who provide specialized counterintelligence coverage of the field army area. The prisoner of war cage section is located with the field army interrogation center for interrogation of prisoners of war and other enemy personnel determined to be of counterintelligence interest. The civil affairs section is deployed with civil affairs units in the field army area. The basic responsibility of the civil affairs section is to interrogate for information of counterintelligence interest, line crossers, and refugees who may be assembled by civil affairs units. The 5 field office teams are normally deployed with 1 team in each corps rear area, 1 team in the field army service area, and 1 team in support of the military intelligence battalion headquarters. More field office teams may be attached, as needed, from the military intelligence group at army group.

WITHIN THE CORPS

The *military intelligence detachment, corps,* provides the corps G2 with assistance in the specialized fields of order of battle, prisoner of war interrogation, document translation, language interpretation, technical intelligence, counterintelligence and photointerpretation. Personnel of this detachment can perform nonspecialized intelligence staff functions in addition to their specialties.

The corps *military intelligence detachment* is assigned to the military intelligence battalion at field army but is attached to the corps. This attachment is for all operations and for certain types of logistical support. When the corps headquarters is transferred to another field army, the military intelligence detachment remains with the corps.

The corps commander normally exercises operational control over the attached detachment through his G2. Operational control of the military intelligence detachment by the corps does not relieve the detachment commander of command. He is responsible for discipline, training, and administration.

The order of battle, photointerpreter, some editorial, and in

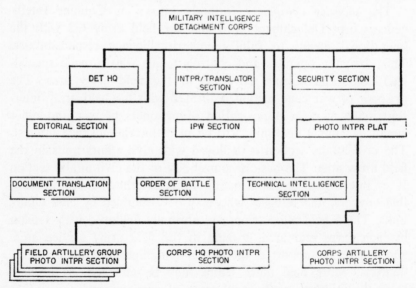

Figure 22. Military intelligence detachment, corps.

some instances, certain technical intelligence and interpreter personnel work within the corps G-2 section. Normally, these individuals receive their guidance and task assignments from the G2 section rather than from the detachment. The detachment commander, however, retains the responsibility for advising the G2 on their proper employment. Information collected by elements of the corps military intelligence detachment is transmitted directly to the G2.

The *editorial section* provides minimum editorial support for the corps G2 section and the corps military intelligence detachment. The *documents translator section* translates and processes documents for the corps G2. The *interpreter/translator section* performs the same functions as described for the corresponding organic platoon in the military intelligence battalion headquarters company. This section provides only minimum interpreter-translator support. Individual augmentation, obtained through military intelligence organization channels, may be required. Personnel of the section participate in staff operations of the corps G2 section when not used for interpreter or translator requirements.

A small IPW section is provided for interrogation of selected prisoners of war.

The *order of battle section* performs all duties pertaining to order of battle functions and arranges for the exchange and dissemination of order of battle information and intelligence among interested elements of the corps and other headquarters. The section is capable of producing current order of battle intelligence and limited special studies within the scope of the order of battle mission.

The *technical intelligence section* assists in the direction and supervision of technical intelligence operations, and supervises technical service intelligence agencies operating in the corps area. It assists special and technical service staff officers, technical service intelligence detachments, and other scientific and technical intelligence agencies. The section maintains certain technical intelligence target lists and collection directives and plans. Individuals of the section supervise, for the corps G2, that portion of the corps collection effort dealing with technical intelligence information. The section recommends and participates in training of subordinate corps elements in technical intelligence matters.

The *security section* (formerly known as Counter Intelligence Corps detachment) provides local security coverage and effects liaison with field army and division security section elements. The efforts of the section are directed by the G2. Additional guidance may be received from higher headquarters through counterintelligence channels.

The *photointerpretation platoon* is organized to provide photointerpretation support for the corps headquarters, corps artillery headquarters, and the separate field artillery groups which may be assigned to the corps. An element of the platoon may be attached to the corps aviation company.

The relationship between the corps detachment and the parent battalion is purely administrative, logistical, and technical. The relationship between the corps detachment and division military intelligence detachments is only technical in nature.

WITHIN THE DIVISION

The *military intelligence detachment, division,* normally supports a division by performing specialized intelligence and counterintelligence functions which require special skills or knowledge of foreign languages. The attachment of this detachment to the division and the relation of the detachment commander to the supported division and the field army military intelligence battalion are the same as discussed under the corps military intelligence detachment.

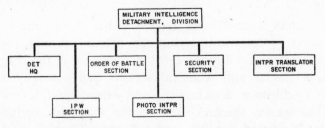

Figure 23. Military intelligence detachment, division.

The *IPW section* is considered the minimum necessary for division interrogation coverage. Interrogator personnel may be temporarily attached to or placed in support of subordinate units. The IPW section has sufficient equipment and transportation to organize 5 mobile interrogation teams and 1 team for employment at the division prisoner of war collecting point. The number of personnel in the IPW team varies in accordance with the situation.

The *photointerpreter section* is normally subdivided to operate at the division headquarters, the division artillery headquarters and the division main airstrip. The senior photointerpretation officer and 1 officer and 3 enlisted assistants normally operate within the division G2 section. One photointerpretation officer and 2 enlisted assistants are normally located at the main division airstrip. One photointerpretation officer and one enlisted assistant are normally attached to the division artillery headquarters. When required, photointerpreter personnel may be attached to other subordinate elements of the division. The photointerpreter personnel may also be used for training intelligence personnel of subordinate units in photointerpretation.

The *security, order of battle,* and *interpreter/translator* sections operate in the same manner as described for the corps military intelligence detachment.

APPENDIX VI

AIR RECONNAISSANCE REQUEST PROCEDURES

Air reconnaissance request procedures depend on whether the request is for a preplanned or an immediate mission. In *preplanned* missions, there is usually at least a day to plan and prepare before the mission is flown. *Immediate* missions must be flown quickly and cannot be planned in advance. From division to field army, all air reconnaissance requests are processed through intelligence (G2 air) channels to the tactical air support section of the tactical operations center. A standard request form is used to make sending requests faster and easier. Figure 24 shows one form.

MISSION PRIORITIES

Usually, the field army headquarters prescribes a uniform

EXPLANATORY NOTES FOR TACTICAL AIR RECONNAISSANCE SUPPORT FORM

SECTION I: To be used by any Army unit requesting tactical air reconnaissance. When transmitting section I by electrical means, only item number and information required will be included.

Item   1 - - - Army mission request number is assigned at division (or higher headquarters when such headquarters originates the request)—per Army SOP.

2 - - - The requesting unit.

3 - - - Requesting unit priority. This priority will be modified, as required, at field army/independent corps prior to forwarding to ASOC.

7 - - - Time information, spot reports, or photos no longer of value.

11 - - - Direction oblique cameras should be facing when exposures are being made.

12 - - - Requesting unit specifies number of prints desired under 12a. Field army/independent corps may indicate 12b and/or 12c. If no printing requirements are indicated, immediate photo report only will be furnished.

15 - - - On artillery adjustment missions all subitems (15a through g) will be completed. On contact reconnaissance missions, subitems 15a through c only.

SECTION II: Completed by Army action agency at any echelon of command.

SECTION III: Completed by Reconnaissance Section, ASOC.

SECTION IV: Item 2 - - - Wing call sign or number.

Item 6 - - - TDP, etc. controlling mission.

Item 7 - - - To indicate point at which Army mission data (section I) will be transmitted to the accomplishing unit.

Explanatory notes on reverse side of tactical air reconnaissance request form (fig. 24).

TACTICAL AIR RECONNAISSANCE SUPPORT FORM
SECTION I ARMY MISSION DATA

1. Army Mission Request No __101__   2. Unit __Powerhouse G2 Air__   3. Priority __2__

4. Type Mission (Photo) (Visual) (Other) __Vis/photo__

5. Target/Area Description Vis: R-1 to Z-51 to R-4 to Z-56 to R-5. Pinpoint photo targets 9, 15, 23, and 26.

6. Time on Target __PM__   7. Time no longer of value __040400 Sep__

8. Specific information/Results desired Suspected enemy armor moving on routes or assembling in areas, or in vicinity of above. Require types of eqpt, direction and speed of movement.

9. Type Photo __V__   10. Scale __Medium__   11. Oblique Camera Direction __N/A__

12. No prints per usable neg: a, ARSB __2__   b, Recce Tech __N/A__   c, Fly Sqdn __N/A__

13. Deliver (Film) (Prints) to: __Powerhouse G2 Air 26Y154367__

14. Spot report required: __Yes__

15. Arty Adj/Contact Recon a, Call Sign __N/A__   b, Prim freq __N/A__   c, Secon Freq __N/A__

d. Firing Unit loc __N/A__   e, Caliber wpn __N/A__   f, Max ordinate __N/A__

g. Effects desired __N/A__

16. Remarks: This request covers preplanned night recon for period 031500—032400 Sep for this unit.

SECTION II ARMY ACTION	SECTION III ASOC ACTION
Received at 'Tiger G2 Air 031545 Sep (Unit-Date-Time)	Received at ASOC ____ (Date-Time)
By __CWK__ Location Checked __CWK__ (Init) (Init-Date-Time)	By ____ Location Checked ____ (Init) (Init-Date-Time)
Coordinated: Arty Air Def Avn __CWK__ (Init)	
Approved/Disapproved __CWK 031600 Sep__ (Init-Date-Time)	Approved/Disapproved ____ (Init-Date-Time)
Reason for disapproval __N/A__	Reason for disapproval ____
Fwd to __Powerhouse__ By __CWK 040400 Sep__ (Unit) (Init-Date-Time) Requesting Unit Notified: __CWK 031800 Sep__ (Init-Date-Time) ARSB notified: __CWK 031800 Sep__ (Init-Date-Time) Addt'l } Print Distr } __Tiger__ __2__ (Unit) (No per neg) ____ (Unit) ____ (No per neg)	Return to Army ____ By ____ (Date - Time) (Init)

SECTION IV AIR MISSION DATA

1. Mission No ____   Army Mission Req No ____

2. Accomplishing Org ____   Notified ____
(Init-Date-Time)

3. Unit Call Sign ____

4. No & Type Aircraft ____   Priority ____

5. TOT ____

6. Control Info ____

7. Army Mission Data ____

8. SCC notified ____
(Init-Date-Time)

9. Other coordination ____
(ALO)   (TDP)

Figure 24. Tactical air reconnaissance request form.

method for air reconnaissance mission priorities. The method includes procedures for reevaluating and screening priorities at each level of command. A common method is to indicate priority by a combination of letter and number reflecting the time and tactical urgency of a specific mission.

REQUESTS FOR PREPLANNED MISSIONS. The *division* G2 air screens requests for preplanned missions from the staff and subordinate units and assigns each mission a priority. He forwards the consolidated requests which cannot be fulfilled by division aviation to the corps G2 air. Missions which can be performed by division aviation are coordinated with the division aviation officer and then forwarded to the aviation company.

The *corps* G2 air screens requests from the divisions, consolidates them with the corps requests, and assigns new priorities. The consolidated corps requests which cannot be fulfilled by corps aviation are forwarded to the G2 air at field army. Missions which can be performed by corps aviation are coordinated with the corps aviation officer and then forwarded to a corps aviation unit.

The *field army* G2 air screens corps requests, consolidates them with those originating at field army and assigns priorities. The requirements which cannot be fulfilled by Army aviation are forwarded to the supporting Services for execution. Missions which can be performed by Army aviation are coordinated with the Army aviation officer and then forwarded to an Army aviation unit. For requests to be executed by a supporting Service, the field army G2 air gives the air reconnaissance support battalion (ARSB) necessary briefing information, priority lists for interpretation of photos, and distribution instructions for photos and photointerpretation reports. The battalion in turn forwards this information to the Army air reconnaissance liaison officers (ARLO's) at the reconnaissance airfields. The field army G2 air informs each corps G2 air of their mission priorities, estimated time over target, assigned mission numbers, and reasons for disapproval of any requests. The corps G2 air in turn, passes the information to the division G2 air.

REQUESTS FOR IMMEDIATE MISSIONS. The procedures

for requesting immediate missions are the same as for preplanned missions except that within the division, a special purpose *air request radio net* is used and division requests are sent direct to the field army G2 air via the air request net. The corps G2 air monitors this air request net and approves division requests by remaining silent. If division requests are sent by means other than the air request net, the corps G2 air is informed immediately.

Units subordinate to a division, brigade, or combat command headquarters request air reconnaissance direct from the division G2 air via the division air request net. Information resulting from executing these requests, if received through the division headquarters, is sent to the brigade and combat command headquarters as well as to the requesting unit.

Air reconnaissance missions using Army aviation, not in direct support, are requested as previously described. When not specifically designated by the requesting unit or the G2 air, the aviation unit selects the equipment to perform the mission. Army aviation photo missions are coordinated by the G2 air with the unit providing photo reproduction facilities, normally the signal battalion. G2 air personnel operate at unit airstrips for briefing and debriefing aviators and observers, disseminating results of air reconnaissance missions, and immediately interpreting photos taken from Army aircraft.

AIR-GROUND COMMUNICATIONS

Communication for Army air-ground operations is provided by a combination of special purpose nets and division and field army area communications systems. *The information net* links the air reconnaissance support battalion, the field Army G2 air, and the corps G2 air, and is used for transmitting information and intelligence. *The Army air request net* links the division, corps and field army G2 air and G3 air and is used for requesting offensive and reconnaissance air support. *The division air request net* links the division and its major subordinate units and is used for requesting offensive and reconnaissance air support. *The air reconnaissance liaison officer* (ARLO) net links the ARLO's, immediate interpretation platoon at the reconnaissance airfields, and the air reconnaissance support battalion. It is used for sending instructions to ARLO's and the immediate interpretation platoon and for sending reports to the air reconnaissance support battalion. *The spot receiver system* consists of organic radio equipment at combat battalion and larger headquarters for monitoring in-flight spot reports on reconnaissance and offensive missions. These radios are also used for emergency communication with the aircraft.

Air-ground communications may vary because of limited availability or effectiveness of equipment and distances between headquarters. Timely transmission of requests and information among all headquarters concerned is required at all times.

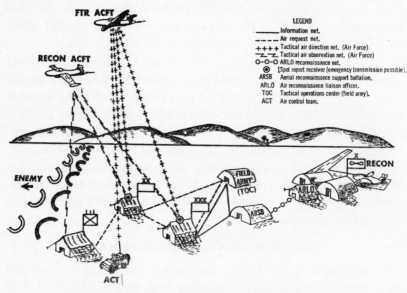

Figure 25. Air-ground communication.

APPENDIX VII

COMBAT SURVEILLANCE EQUIPMENT AND USE

Different kinds of combat surveillance equipment are being developed by many nations. United States Army combat surveillance equipment are short, medium, and long range ground radars and airborne devices. The airborne devices are cameras, radars, and infrared devices mounted either in drones or manned aircraft. Ground infrared and sound detectors are under development.

GROUND SURVEILLANCE RADARS

Ground surveillance radars detect and track moving targets such as vehicles and personnel by distinctive tones heard through the operator's headset. In addition to the operator tracking the targets by hand, medium and long range ground radars can be set to automatically scan a preselected area. Short range ground radars can detect moving vehicle targets out to about 6,000 meters. Medium range ground radars can detect such targets out to about 10,000 meters. Long range ground radars are effective at even greater ranges. While ground surveillance radars can usually be hand carried, the long range radar is usually carried in light trucks.

AIRBORNE RADARS

Airborne ground surveillance radars are fixed into liaison or tion or side looking. The *high resolution* radar is used mostly for area coverage to detect fixed targets. The *side-looking* radar is used mostly to search for moving targets up to about 40 miles distant.

Airborne ground surveillance radars are fixed in to liaison or light aircraft.

AIRBORNE INFRARED

The typical airborne infrared ground surveillance device, also fixed into a liaison or light aircraft, detects the presence of hot objects which indicate traveled routes, vehicles, bivouacs, weapons, and similar activities and installations. Airborne infrared devices can detect hot objects out to about 30 miles, depending on the tracking technique used.

DRONES

Drones, or unmanned radio controlled miniature aircraft are used to carry cameras and other surveillance devices over guided or preselected courses or areas. Drones are limited in range and flight duration. At the end of each mission they are recovered by use of a parachute release. A radar tracking and plotting system is used to guide the drone. The same system is also used to guide manned aircraft carrying airborne surveillance devices during conditions of reduced visibility.

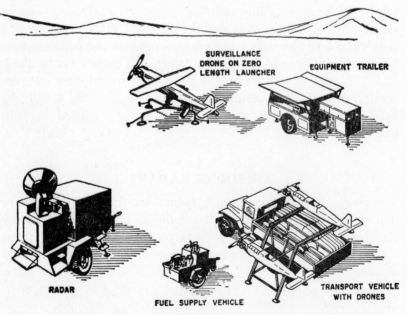

Figure 26. Typical drone system.

Figure 27. Short range ground radar.

Figure 28. Medium range ground radar.

Figure 29. Long range ground radar.

Figure 30. Airborne side-looking radar.

EMPLOYMENT OF GROUND RADARS

ASSIGNMENT. Usually, enough short range ground radars are assigned to battle groups, regiments, and to reconnaissance and combat battalions to permit attaching one radar to each line company. These radars are either attached to the line companies or employed under the control of the unit intelligence officer. Medium range ground radars are usually assigned to battle groups, regiments, and to separate reconnaissance and combat battalions. These radars are usually employed under the control of the unit intelligence officer to add depth to the area under radar surveillance. Long range ground radars are usually assigned to the division artillery headquarters battery for locating more distant targets. The long range ground radar is usually under the control of the division artillery intelligence officer.

RADAR POSITIONS. All ground surveillance radars depend on line of sight and require a background to detect movement. Consequently, they are placed on terrain like that required for observation posts and as far forward as possible. They usually operate only during conditions of poor visibility. Radar teams must be given specific instructions to include the areas to be covered, frequency of coverage, and the scanning method to be used, such as area scan or point scan. The area or points to be covered depend on the terrain, enemy capabilities, equipment capabilities, and the desired overlap in coverage by adjacent radars.

Ground surveillance radar positions must be accurately located, so that map locations of detected activities can be accurately reported. Orientation of radar set positions and determination of surveillance areas on the ground are done during daylight when possible.

RADAR SURVEILLANCE CARDS. Radar surveillance cards are prepared and distributed to the unit intelligence officer and, if requested, to the intelligence officer of the next higher headquarters.

SURVEILLANCE PLAN. The intelligence officer of the unit equipped with surveillance equipment prepares a plan for their use. This plan is based on the mission of the unit, the capabilities of the available equipment, and the nature of the terrain. A plan of this type makes it easier to insure that the full capabilities of surveillance equipment are used to gather the information required.

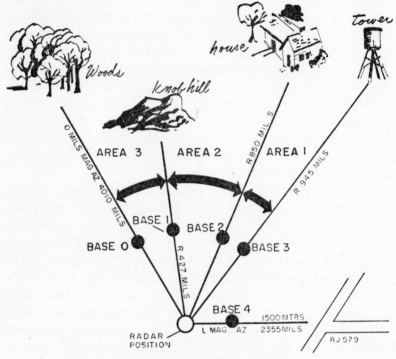

Figure 31. Radar surveillance card.

TACTICAL USE. In the offense, ground surveillance radars are used for surveillance forward of the line of contact and to the flanks. These radars can also be used to guide friendly attacking forces and patrols during periods of poor visibility and to keep critical areas and dangerous avenues of approach under surveillance. Short range radars are usually attached to the attacking companies. In the defense, ground surveillance radars are used to watch over likely avenues of approach, gaps between units, and critical areas. Radars may be attached to forward security elements. In retrograde operations and withdrawals, ground surveillance radar sites in the new areas are selected in advance. If possible, these positions and tentative radar surveillance cards are prepared in advance. Usually only short range ground radars are attached to detachments left in contact.

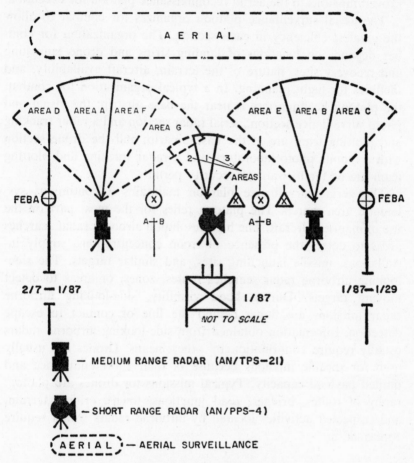

Figure 32. Surveillance plan.

AERIAL SURVEILLANCE PLATOON

The airborne surveillance devices, drones, and radar tracking and plotting system are usually in an aerial surveillance platoon in the aviation company of a division or regiment. The platoon normally operates under the control of the G2/S2 air. Missions to be performed by the platoon are requested by the staff and by subordinate, higher, and neighboring units. Missions are either preplanned or immediate as explained in Appendix VI, "Air Reconnaissance Request Procedures." The G2/S2 Air sends approved missions to the aerial reconnaissance platoon for execution.

The aerial surveillance platoon organizes for combat to allow the greatest efficiency in each section. The organization for combat depends on locations of landing strips and drone launching and recovery sites, nature of the terrain, aircraft availability, and facilities for flight planning. In a typical organization for combat, the platoon headquarters is near the base airstrip; the visual and photo surveillance section, aerial radar section and a radar tracking and plotting team are at the base airstrip; and the drone section with a mobile photo laboratory and a radar tracking and plotting team are as far forward as security permits.

The aerial surveillance platoon maintains a continuous systematic area search. The platoon relies for the most part on the use of manned aircraft. The high resolution airborne radar searches areas to detect the presence of troop concentrations, supply installations, missile launching sites, and similar targets. The side-looking airborne radar searches routes, zones, or areas to detect moving targets. During good visibility, side-looking airborne radar missions are flown behind the line of contact to escape detection. Information obtained from side-looking airborne radars usually require confirmation by other means. Drones are usually used for specific missions because of their short endurance and limited payload capacity. Typical missions for drones are photography of routes, bridges, road junctions, towns, critical terrain, and suspected activities located by airborne radars which require confirmation.

APPENDIX VIII

STANDARD SHELLING, MORTARING, BOMBING, AND TOXIC REPORT, AND NUCLEAR BURST REPORT

SHELREP, MORTREP, BOMREP, TOXREP (state which)

A. FROM: (unit, use current call-sign address group or code name).

B. POSITION OF OBSERVER: grid reference preferred. (Encode if this discloses location of a headquarters or important observation post.)

C. GRID OR MAGNETIC: (state which) BEARING OR AZIMUTH OF FLASH OR SOUND OR GROOVE OF SHELL: (state which) IN MILS OR DEGREES: (state which) ORIGIN OF FLIGHT PATH: (missiles). (Omit for aircraft)

D. TIME FROM: ....

E. TIME TO: ....

F. AREA SHELLED, MORTARED, BOMBED, OR CONTAMINATED: (May be sent either):

   (1) Bearing/azimuth (in degrees or mils—state which) and distance (in yards or meters—state which) from observer.

   (2) Grid reference (clear reference may be used consistent with security requirements). (See note 2c, below.)

   NOTE: Where method (1) is used, maximum accuracy possible is essential.

G. NUMBER AND NATURE OF GUNS, MORTARS, AIRCRAFT, OR OTHER METHODS OF DELIVERY:

H. NATURE OF FIRE: (registration, bombardment, harassment, etc.). (May be omitted for aircraft.)

I. NUMBER AND TYPE OF SHELLS, BOMBS, TOXIC AGENTS, ETC.:

J. TIME OF FLASH TO BANG: (omit for aircraft).

K. DAMAGE: (optional). (May include both effects and casualties in the case of toxic attack.)

NOTES

1. *Code Word.* Each transmission will be preceded by one of the following code words:

   SHELREP (in the case of enemy cannon or missile fire).

   MORTREP (in the case of enemy mortar fire).

   BOMREP (in the case of enemy air attack).

   TOXREP (in the case of enemy toxic attack).

143

2. *Security:* The message is always transmitted in clear except for the following:

a. The originating unit (heading A) for which the current call-sign, address group, or equivalent is used when the message is sent by radio.

b. The location of the observer (heading B) is in code if sent by radio and if it discloses the location of a headquarters or important observation post.

c. The originator may consider that the conditions prevailing warrant classifying the entire message.

d. Damage (heading K) is not sent in the clear.

3. *Headings:* Each heading of the format is given a capital letter which makes for ease of communication. The heading itself is NOT transmitted. Headings of the format which cannot be completed or are not applicable will be omitted in the transmission of the report.

4. *Transmission:* Reports will be transmitted by the fastest means available, using the format given above.

EXAMPLE, SHELREP

ALFA	OSCAR PAPA 1
BRAVO	UNIFORM TANGO 365478
CHARLIE	GRID AZIMUTH FLAS 1,438 MILS
DELTA	1252
ECHO	1257
FOXTROT	UNIFORM TANGO 378543
GOLF	2 UNKNOWN
HOTEL	HARASSMENT
INDIA	18 UNKNOWN
JULIETT	3 SECONDS
KILO	NEGLIGIBLE

NUCLEAR BURST REPORT

LINE
NR

1. UNIT OF ORIGIN: (use current call-sign, address group or code name).
2. POSITION OF OBSERVER: (grid coordinates preferred—encode if this discloses the location of a unit, headquarters, or important observation post).
3. TYPE OF OBSERVATION: (report type of instrument(s), if any, used to obtain data).
4. TIME OF BURST: ....
5. GROUND ZERO: (measured within 15 seconds using stem of cloud for location)—either:
   a. Coordinates (grid).

b. Azimuth (magnetic, from position of observer, in degrees or mils— state which).

c. Polar coordinates.

6. HEIGHT OF BURST: (measured with special instruments or estimated)—either:

a. Height, measured (in meters).

b. Vertical angle, measured (in degrees or mils—state which).

c. Estimated height (high, low, or surface).

7. CLOUD TOP: (measured after cloud stabilization; about 10 minutes after burst)—either:

a. Height (in meters).

b. Vertical angle (in degrees or mils—state which).

8. CLOUD DIAMETER: (measured after cloud stabilization about 10 minutes after burst)—either:

a. Diameter (in meters).

b. Subtended angle (in degrees or mils—state which).

9. WEAPON YIELD: (report only if measured by special instrument).

10. WEAPON EFFECTS AT LOCATION OF OBSERVER (indicate the effects of the burst on the personnel and equipment in the vicinity of the observer. This should be brief. It may be used to help determine weapon yield and to estimate the damage produced by the burst).

INSTRUCTIONS:

a. Transmit available data promptly (encode appropriate portions as required by SSI or SOP).

(1) Transmit burst location data (lines 5 and 6) immediately after measurement; do not wait until cloud measurements are made.

(2) Transmit cloud data (lines 7 and 8) immediately after measurement.

b. Make message brief.

c. Transmit by line number only those lines of the above format for which data is available.

d. If a line item is based on an estimate, indicate this in the report by prefacing the data with the word "estimated."

EXAMPLE NUCLEAR BURST REPORT

LINE 1 —BLACK BEAR CHARLIE

LINE 2 —48635904

LINE 3 —AIMING CIRCLE

LINE 4 —100945Z

LINE 5B—165 MILS

LINE 6C—ESTIMATED LOW

LINE 10 —BLAST WAVE CARRIED STONES UP TO ONE-QUARTER INCH IN SIZE. SMALL BRANCHES BROKEN FROM TREES. SOME PERSONNEL BURNED ON BARE SKIN.

APPENDIX IX

WEATHER AND CLIMATE INTELLIGENCE AND INFORMATION

Summaries of weather and climate are *information* summaries used as a basis for other estimates and plans. They are usually prepared by the supporting Air Weather Service detachments as requested by the intelligence officer. The summaries are disseminated by the intelligence officer and may be included as annexes to intelligence documents such as written analyses of the area of operations, intelligence estimates, and periodic intelligence reports (PERINTREP).

WEATHER SUMMARY

A weather summary is a description of the weather at a point, along a route, or within an area during a specified recent period. Weather summaries are used in analyzing the effects of weather on recent operations and in estimating the effects of weather on future operations. They are required for engineer forecasts of stream flow, condition of ground, and trafficability.

CLIMATIC SUMMARY

A climatic summary gives statistical data in terms of averages, extremes, and frequencies of occurrence for a specified period of time such as a year, season, month, at a given point, along a route, or within an area. Climatic summaries are compiled from historical records of weather observations over long periods. An example is given at the end of this appendix.

CLIMATIC STUDY

A climatic study is the analysis and interpretation of climatic information (climatic summary) in the light of probable effects on operations. Climatic studies are usually prepared at corps and higher headquarters. Detailed climatic studies for strategic areas of the world are in the *National Intelligence Survey*. The supporting air weather service unit, at the request of the intelligence officer, prepares climatic studies for specific areas. The intelligence officer interprets and refines these climatic studies to meet the requirements of the command. Climatic studies are disseminated in the same manner as weather and climate summaries.

WEATHER FORECAST

A weather forecast is a prediction of the weather conditions expected at a place, within an area, or along a route at a specified future time, or during a specified period. The accuracy and reliability of weather forecasts depend upon factors such as characteristics of the forecast area, available weather data, reliability of weather communications facilities, forecast period length, and the experience of the forecaster. Reliability of forecasts generally decreases as the forecast period increases. Weather forecasts are in *coded* (numerical), *graphical* (pictorial), or *written* (plain language) format. Weather forecasts for use by troop units are usually in plain language form. Forecasts are classified as short period, extended period, and long period. A short period forecast covers up to 48 hours in advance of the time of issue. Short period forecasts are also referred to by the length of the period covered, such as "12-hour," "24-hour," or "48-hour" forecasts. An extended period forecast covers a period of from 3 to 5 days, and a long period forecast covers a period more than 5 days in advance of the time of issue. Because of their changing nature, timeliness is the critical factor in disseminating weather forecasts. This is especially true of short range forecasts. Weather forecasts are normally transmitted by electrical means. Figure 33 shows the contents of weather forecasts and figure 34 shows a typical extended period forecast.

SEVERE WEATHER WARNINGS. The intelligence officer also ensures dissemination of severe weather warnings. These are special forecasts of hazardous weather to enable units to take necessary action to prevent injury to personnel and damage to materiel. The type of weather for which severe weather warnings are issued depends on the needs of the unit. Severe weather warnings usually cover tornadoes, thunderstorms, dust or sand storms, extremely heavy precipitation, freezing temperatures, winds above specified speeds, and freezing precipitation. They are issued by the supporting air weather service detachment as requested. Flood warnings are the responsibility of the unit engineer. Severe weather warnings are normally disseminated as flash reports.

CURRENT WEATHER REPORTS. Current weather reports contain information on existing weather conditions or specific weather elements. They may be oral, written, or a graphic representation. They are made by Army aviators, field artillery

	3-5 day forecast[1]	48-hour forecast	24-hour forecast	12-hour forecast[2]	12-hour flight forecast for aviation	Route and terminal forecasts for individual army aviation flights[4]	Forecasts for use of nuclear weapons	Radiological defense forecasts
Cloud coverage—height and amount in general terms	X	X						
Cloud coverage—height in feet above ground and amount in eights of sky			X	X	X	X	X	
Temperatures in degrees centigrade, wind direction to nearest 10 degrees, and wind speed to nearest 5 knots at 2,000-foot intervals from surface to 30,000 feet					X	X		
Precipitation, type, character, intensity, time of beginning, and duration	X	X	X	X	X	X	X	
Weather phenomena to include items such as tornadoes, thunderstorms, squalls, blowing dust, blowing sand, and fog.		X	X	X	X	X		
Visibility—in units of distance with restrictive elements	X	X	X	X	X3	X3	X	
General wind pattern	X							
Temperature ranges including freeze and thaw	X	X	X	X				
Surface winds—general direction and speed		X	X	X				
Relative humidity—stated as low, medium, high	X							
Relative humidity—stated in percentages			X	X			X	
Terminal conditions at specific terminals to include ceiling in feet above ground, airstrip visibility, precipitation, surface winds, temperature, and dew point					X	X		
Density altitude—information required established in local SOP					X	X		
Thickness of cloud decks in feet					X	X	X	
Frontal conditions							X	
Altitude of tropopause in feet							X	X
Temperature in degrees centigrade, wind direction to nearest 10 degrees, and wind speed to nearest 5 knots at 6,000 feet intervals from surface to 102,000 feet.[5]							X	X
Atmospheric Pressure		X	X	X	X	X	X	X

[1]Time of significant changes in weather elements should be given, when possible.
[2]This forecast gives weather conditions along the forward edge of the battle area. It should be subdivided, as appropriate, for the battle groups, regiments, and battalions concerned.
[3]At flight altitudes.
[4]Information is for a specified route for a specific period. Additional information required are altimeter settings at destination and alternate strip.
[5]Surface to 60,000 feet each 2 hours and surface to 102,000 feet each 6 hours.

Figure 33. Contents of weather forecasts.

observation units, artillery and air defense meteorological sections, and air weather service detachments. Other units furnish current weather reports as directed. Reports of current weather are used in connection with operations of aircraft, use of artillery, nuclear weapons, chemical and biological agents, and other activities. Normally, these reports are sent direct to the user by the collection agency.

EXTENDED PERIOD FORECAST HILDAWOODS AND VICINITY VALID 01/0600Z TO 04/0600Z: 1 AUG: SKY CONDITION OVERCAST CEILING 5000 FEET (ABOVE TERRAIN) GRADUALLY LOWERING TO 1000 FEET BY SUNSET. VIS-IBILITY 5 MILES IN HAZE OCCASIONALLY LOWERING TO 2 MILES IN RAIN. WINDS NORTHEAST 3 TO 5 KNOTS. MIN TEMP RANGE 50° TO 60°F MAX 65° TO 75°F. 2 AUG: SKY CONDITION GENERALLY 500 TO 1000 FEET OVER-CAST IMPROVING TO 2000 FEET SCATTERED BY SUNSET. VISIBILITY 1 TO 2 MILES IN LIGHT RAIN AND FOG BECOMING OVER 7 MILES BY NOON. WINDS NORTHEAST 5 TO 10 KNOTS BECOMING SOUTHWEST 10 TO 15 KNOTS BY MIDAFTERNOON. WARMER MIN TEMP 55° TO 65°F MAX 70° TO 80°F. 3 AUG: SKY CONDITION CLEAR VISIBILITY 10 TO 15 MILES WIND SOUTHWEST 15 KNOTS. LITTLE CHANGE MIN TEMP MAX RANGE 75° TO 85°F. LIGHT DATA: 1 AUG: MORNING NAUTICAL TWILIGHT 01/1151Z, EVENING NAUTI-CAL TWILIGHT 02/0240Z. MOON PHASE: FULL. MOONRISE 02/0230Z, MOON-SET 02/1350Z. 2 AUG: MORNING NAUTICAL TWILIGHT 02/1152Z, EVENING NAUTICAL TWILIGHT 03/0239Z. 3 AUG: MORNING NAUTICAL TWILIGHT 03/1153Z, EVENING NAUTICAL TWILIGHT 04/0228Z. PLANNING DATA FOR RADIOLOGICAL FALLOUT: 1 AUG: 0–12000 SOUTH 10 TO 20 KNOTS, 12000–24000 SOUTH TO SOUTHWEST 15 TO 30 KNOTS, 24000–36000 SOUTHWEST 20 TO 40 KNOTS, 36000–48000 SOUTHWEST 35 TO 55 KNOTS, 48000–60000 SOUTH-WEST TO WEST 50 TO 70 KNOTS. 2 AUG: 0–12000 SOUTHWEST 15 TO 40 KNOTS, 12000–24000 SOUTHWEST 25 TO 55 KNOTS, 24000–36000 SOUTHWEST 40 TO 75 KNOTS, 36000–48000 SOUTHWEST TO WEST 30 TO 40 KNOTS, 48000–60000 SOUTHWEST TO WEST 25 TO 35 KNOTS. 3 AUG: 0–12000 WEST TO NORTHWEST 20 TO 30 KNOTS, 12000–24000 WEST TO SOUTHWEST 35 TO 50 KNOTS, 24000–36000 WEST TO SOUTHWEST 50 TO 80 KNOTS, 36000–48000 WEST 25 TO 35 KNOTS, 48000–60000 WEST 20 TO 30 KNOTS.

Figure 34. Typical extended period weather forecast.

EXAMPLE OF A CLIMATIC SUMMARY FOR THE MONTH OF JULY, 3D CORPS AREA

1. GENERAL CIRCULATION: Generally air flows from the west and northwest. Occasionally warm, dry, continental air from Russia causes a relatively intense, dry heat with temperatures 90° or more.

2. TEMPERATURES: Afternoon temperatures generally are in the 70's and morning temperatures are in the 50's. There are occasional periods of hot, dry spells that last more than a week with temperatures in the 90's. The highest temperature ever recorded was 101° F.

3. THUNDERSTORMS: Occur frequently and usually develop during the day with intensity in the late afternoon and evening.

4. SURFACE WINDS: Average wind speed is 5.8 MPH. The predominant direction is northeast, with a mean speed of 8.4 MPH. The

strongest mean wind is from the east-northeast 10.0 MPH. Calms occur 25.2 percent of the time, and usually in the early morning. Calms or near calms often last the whole day.

5. CLOUDINESS: Mornings frequently are clear. Clouds develop by noon with maximum cloud cover in the late afternoon, decreasing to zero just before sunset.

6. VISIBILITY: Normal visibilities are 7 to 13 miles and occasionally further. Occasional haze may reduce visibility to about 3 miles.

7. PRECIPITATION: Thunderstorms are the usual cause of precipitation. Occasionally a southwesterly wind will cause continued drizzle and low, overcast skies for 1 to 3 days. This is the only time low visibilities occur.

MEAN PRECIPITATION, DAYS WITH THUNDERSTORM, TEMPERATURES, AND FOG, JUNE, JULY, AUGUST AND ANNUALLY

	Jun	Jul	Aug	Annual	Years Recorded
Mean precipitation (inches)	2.56	2.48	2.36	26.97	40
Mean number of days with thunderstorm ...	4	4	3	18	11
Temperature (°F)					
Absolute max	95	101	97		10
Absolute min	50	43	43		10
Mean daily max ..	71	74	73		40
Mean daily min ..	51	55	53		60
Mean number of days with fog	2	2	4	57	11

PERCENTAGE FREQUENCY OF SURFACE WINDS BY DIRECTION AND AVERAGE WIND SPEEDS IN KNOTS FOR THE MONTH OF JULY

	S	SSW	SW	WSW	W	WNW	NW	NNW
Percentage frequency of direction	2.1	2.0	8.6	1.0	0.7	0.3	0.4	0.0
Average speed by direction	5.6	9.4	8.8	7.6	6.8	8.3	3.2	0.0

	N	NNE	NE	ENE	E	ESE	SE	SSE
Percentage frequency of direction	1.2	2.1	19.5	10.9	12.2	2.7	9.6	1.0
Average speed by direction	5.0	6.3	8.4	10.1	7.1	6.6	6.0	4.0

APPENDIX X

DISSEMINATION OF SPECIALIZED INFORMATION AND INTELLIGENCE

PHOTOINTERPRETATION REPORTS

Photointerpretation reports may be spot reports, notes on paragraphs, or in a prescribed format. The basic types of photo-interpretation reports are immediate, mission review, summary, detailed, and special.

IMMEDIATE REPORTS. Immediate reports are *written* and supplement oral spot reports when wide dissemination or written confirmation of an oral spot report is required. An immediate report does not have a prescribed form.

MISSION REVIEW REPORTS. Mission review reports have a prescribed form and are prepared on each airphoto mission flown by a supporting Service. They contain a summary of the information on installations, activities, and areas photographed for the first time, or on changes which have occurred since the last previous photo was taken. These reports are distributed to units which will not require further photointerpretation or which do not have trained photointerpreters. Mission review reports are prepared and disseminated by the air reconnaissance support battalion, usually within 48 hours, in accordance with procedures established by the field army G2. Mission review reports provide a basis for order of prints or requests for detailed reports described below.

SUMMARY REPORTS. Summary reports consolidate information from earlier photo reports by category and time period, develop trends and patterns pertaining to targets covered, and describe the current status of the targets. These reports are valuable in acquiring targets deep in enemy held areas. Summary reports are normally prepared by the air reconnaissance support battalion as requested.

DETAILED REPORTS. Detailed reports give complete infor-

151

mation on individual targets or areas for use in strategic and tactical planning. They contain detailed and precise information developed from close study of aerial photographs and other intelligence sources. These reports are prepared as required at corps and higher echelons.

SPECIAL REPORTS. Special reports are used to present information not included in the above photointerpretation reports. Special reports treat a subject or a related group of subjects thoroughly and normally require considerable time to prepare. These reports are prepared as required at corps and higher headquarters.

PRISONER OF WAR INTERROGATION AND TRANSLATION REPORTS

These reports summarize, or report in full, the results of interrogation of one or more prisoners of war, and translations of extracts or summaries of enemy documents. Information of immediate value is disseminated as a spot report. Other information is disseminated in the most convenient form, considering the needs of the users. At corps and higher headquarters, detailed reports of these types are usually distributed as annexes to the PERINTREP.

TECHNICAL INTELLIGENCE BULLETINS AND SUMMARIES

These are reports used to disseminate the results of examination of enemy materiel. Bulletins usually deal with individual items, and summaries are broader in scope. They are disseminated either through command channels, technical intelligence channels, or technical service channels, depending on the scope and nature of the contents.

ORDER OF BATTLE BOOKS AND HANDBOOKS

Order of battle *books* contain lists, histories, code names, and other data on foreign units, and biographical data on foreign military personalities. Order of battle *handbooks* contain data concerning the political structure, military system and organization, and tactical doctrine of foreign nations. Order of battle books and handbooks are usually prepared by the Departments of the Army, Navy, and Air Force and theater headquarters. A field army may issue supplements to keep these documents current.

RADIOLOGICAL CONTAMINATION ESTIMATES AND REPORTS

These are prepared and disseminated at division and higher headquarters within the field army, by the chemical, biological, and radiological section of the tactical operations center. Reports of radiological contamination information are usually in the form of current or future contamination charts. The *current contamination chart* is a plot of dose rate contours of operational interest extracted from the radiation situation map. In *future contamination charts,* decay factors are applied to estimate the radiation situation at later times. Current and future contamination charts are disseminated to interested staff sections, agencies, and other headquarters.

Fallout predictions are scale plots which indicate only the possible danger areas from fallout. Dose rates are *not* predicted. The plots contain earliest times of arrival points. They may also depict the *hot line,* the probable time of ending of fallout, and the general area of contaminated air which is of interest to aircraft or which may be affected by rainout. The hot line extends to any distance from ground zero through points of maximum dose rate and roughly describes the axis of the fallout pattern. The dose rate generally decreases downward along this line and radially away from it. Radiation predictions are based on current or forecast meteorological data and actual or assumed ground zero, yield, height of burst, and cloud data. Fallout predictions provide information which is used as a basis for planning and estimates. Fallout predictions from enemy or friendly use of nuclear weapons, before and after the burst, are prepared in the chemical, biological, and radiological section of the tactical operations center or similar agency. Fallout predictions resulting from enemy use of nuclear weapons, actual or assumed, are distributed by the chemical, biological, and radiological section as directed by the intelligence officer to interested staff officers, agencies and subordinate units.

MAPS

Maps are intelligence documents and not normal supply items. Divisions requisition and draw their maps from corps, and not directly from the field army, as with supply items.

STAFF RESPONSIBILITIES. The intelligence officer is responsible for staff supervision of all activities concerning military topographic surveys and maps, including acquisition, reproduction, storage, and distribution. The engineer is responsible for the procurement, storage, reproduction, and distribution of military maps and allied materials, to include trig lists and gazeteers, under the staff supervision of the intelligence officer.

Changes in tactical plans affect the map requirements. The distribution system must respond rapidly to such changes if the proper maps are to be provided in time. In fast moving situations, issuing maps to individuals and small units is difficult. The bulk of maps needed to cover a large area makes it impracticable to supply a unit with maps for a prolonged, fast-moving operation. Logistical limitations prevent the maintenance of large reserves of maps.

Timely planning ensures that sufficient quantities of suitable maps are available when and where needed. Map planning is governed by area of coverage scales, and allowances for the maps required. The intelligence officer, the operations officer, and the engineer plan the unit map requirements. Based on operational plans, the intelligence officer and the operations officer decide on the types and scales of maps to be used. The engineer advises on the availability of maps, including types and scales. Unit boundaries are projected by the G3 to indicate the area for which coverage is desired. For tactical units, this area usually extends forward to include at least the *area of influence*. It is desirable to include coverage of the area of interest. The unit engineer calculates actual map requirements based on this information and allowance tables.

COVERAGE. Map coverage is the number of sheets of the same scale required to cover the area considered and adjacent areas. An armored division in corps reserve usually requires coverage of the entire corps area and the areas of divisions adjacent to the corps. For computation purposes, a map sheet is required by a unit if more than 20 percent of the area of the sheet is in the unit area of operations. Overlap is required for planning and coordination. The number of map sheets required at each scale is determined from a map index. The required map coverage is marked on the index and the sheets included within the area are counted and listed by appropriate identification symbols.

SCALE. Map scale requirements are influenced by the nature of the friendly forces, character of the terrain, and type of operations. Small-scale maps are used for general planning and for strategic studies. Large-scale maps are used for technical and tactical needs. Maps covering the area of present and projected operations are of as large a scale as necessary to provide the details required. Coverage outside the unit area of operations usually is of smaller scale.

ALLOWANCES. Map allowances are based on tables published by the theater or theater Army headquarters. These tables specify types of maps and quantities authorized according to map scale and type of unit. These tables, used in conjunction with inventories of available maps, provide a distribution guide for a particular type and scale map. An initial issue of maps is based upon the initial allowances set forth in the tables described above. It is the number of copies of map sheets, by type or scale, which can be requisitioned by units without requiring approval by higher headquarters. A replenishment issue is based upon prescribed replenishment allowances. It includes authorized supplemental issues to cover normal losses. Replenishment requirements are calculated by applying a percentage factor to the number of copies in the initial issue. Emergency issues are made as required to meet unforeseen needs.

APPENDIX XI

FORMAT AND EXAMPLE OF INTELLIGENCE SUMMARY (ISUM)

FORMAT

(NOTE: Omit items not applicable unless otherwise indicated.)

1. Issuing unit.
2. Time and date of issue.
3. Summary of enemy activity for period.
   a. Ground activity.
   b. Trace of forward elements.
   c. Potential nuclear targets.
   d. Air activity.
   e. Nuclear activity.
   f. Other (new tactics, counterintelligence, etc.).
4. Personnel and equipment losses.
   a. Personnel (KIA, WIA).
   b. Prisoners of war.
   c. Equipment destroyed or captured.

FM CG 20TH INF DIV
TO CG I ST CORPS **OPERATIONAL IMMEDIATE**

ISUM NUMBER 144 ENDING 040600. PARA 3A. AGGRESSOR CONTINUED DEFENSE IN ZONE EXCEPT FOR LOCAL ATTACK AT 0415 VICINITY R376759 WITH ESTIMATED 90 MEN, 3 MEDIUM TANKS, AND LIGHT ARTILLERY SUPPORT. ATTACK REPULSED. PARA 3D. ATTACK SUPPORTED BY 2 JET ATTACK AIRPLANES BOMBING AND STRAFING VICINITY R396756 FOR 5 MINUTES STARTING AT 0425. PARA 3E. ATTACK PRECEDED AT 0410 BY VERY HIGH AIR BURST NUCLEAR WEAPON, GROUND ZERO R374761, DELIVERY MEANS UNDETERMINED, YIELD ESTIMATED AT 0.5 KT. PARA 4A. CONFIRMED 20 KIA, ESTIMATED 5 KIA, ESTIMATED 30 WIA. PARA 4B. 10 INCLUDING 2 WIA. PARA 4C. 2 MEDIUM TANKS DESTROYED, 1 DAMAGED, 1 JET ATTACK AIRCRAFT SHOT DOWN. PARA 6. PRISONER STATES AMMUNITION SUPPLY IN FORWARD UNITS RUNNING LOW (C-3). PARA 7A. PATROL REPORTS BATTERY 150 MM HOWITZERS AT R303292. PRISONERS CONFIRM LOCATION 2D BATTALION, 17 RIFLE REGIMENT VICINITY R375758 (B-1) PARA 8 AIRBORNE RADAR RECONNAISSANCE DETECTED 10 TRUCKS MOVING SOUTH ON ROAD AT R330280 AT 0345. PARA 9 PROBABLY ROUTINE SUPPLY VEHICLES PARA 10 SNOW STARTED AT 040545 AND CONTINUING. GROUND FROZEN HARD AND SUPPORTS ALL TYPES OF VEHICLES. PARA 11 LOCAL ATTACK REPORTED PROBABLY WAS TO SEIZE HILL 405. ENEMY IS CAPABLE OF CONTINUING DEFENSE IN PRESENT POSITION, MAKING LOCAL ATTACKS TO IMPROVE HIS DEFENSIVE POSITION, WITHDRAWING TO STRONGER POSITION ALONG LAURIEX RIVER. PARA 12 CONTINUED DEFENSE IN PRESENT POSITION MOST PROBABLE.

Figure 35. Example of a division ISUM (full distribution not included).

5. New obstacles and barriers.
6. Administrative activities.
7. New identifications.
   a. Units.
   b. Personalities.
8. Enemy movements.
9. Estimate number and types of vehicles.
10. Weather and terrain conditions.
11. Brief discussion of capabilities and vulnerabilities (always included).
12. Conclusions (always included and should, if possible, be approved by the commander).

APPENDIX XII

FORMAT AND EXAMPLE OF A PERIODIC INTELLIGENCE REPORT (PERINTREP)

Copy Nr
Unit
Location
Date, time, group
Message Reference Nr

PERINTREP NR:
Period Covered:
Reference: (maps or charts)
Disposal instructions: (if any)

1. GENERAL ENEMY SITUATION: A brief summary of enemy operations and may contain a reference to an annex showing potential nuclear targets developed or continuing during the period. Amplifying details are furnished in the paragraphs which follow. This paragraph provides a quick briefing on the highlights of the enemy situation and the significance of the enemy's major activities to include *marked* changes in morale, strength, dispositions, tactics, combat efficiency, and equipment. Data which are lengthy or can conveniently be shown graphically are presented in annexes.

2. ENEMY OPERATIONS DURING PERIOD: Contains the details of the intelligence summarized in paragraph 1. Detailed intelligence on strengths and dispositions of enemy units, order of battle, reserve, and reinforcements; new enemy tactics, weapons, and equipment, are included in this paragraph if there is no order of battle annex.

Much of paragraph 2 may be presented graphically by overlays, printed maps, sketch maps, and as annexes. Similarly, order of battle reports and other intelligence documents are frequently disseminated as annexes to which reference is made in the appropriate subparagraph of paragraph 2. Subparagraphs are omitted when appropriate intelligence is lacking.

    a. Strengths and dispositions.
    b. Order of battle.
    c. Reserves and reinforcements.
    d. New enemy tactics, weapons, and equipment.
    e. Air forces.
    f. Administrative units.
    g. Airborne units.

h. Antiaircraft defenses.

i. Antitank units.

j. Armored units.

k. Artillery (including rockets.)

l. Cavalry.

m. Nuclear, biological, chemical, electronic, or radiological warfare.

n. Engineers.

o. Guerrilla.

p. Guided missiles.

q. Infantry.

r. Reconnaissance.

s. Other elements (list alphabetically in separate subparagraphs).

3. OTHER INTELLIGENCE FACTORS: When only limited distribution of the information and intelligence is required or the material is detailed, it is preferable to publish the material in an annex or appendix. Data covered in other parts of the report are not repeated in this paragraph.

a. Enemy identifications (show in tabular form).

(1) Confirmed:

Unit	Location	Time	Source

(2) Unconfirmed:

Unit	Location	Time	Source

b. Enemy organization and strength/combat efficiency. (Usually shown in an annex or appendix).

c. Equipment.

d. Personalities.

e. Casualties.

f. Morale.

g. Enemy defenses, minefields, fortifications, barriers, obstacles, and other defensive works. (Show on maps or overlays if possible.)

h. Details of administrative installations and support.

i. Terrain. (Use an annex, special maps, and overlays where possible).

j. Weather.

k. Any pertinent factors not otherwise covered.

4. COUNTERINTELLIGENCE: This paragraph, or parts thereof, is best issued as an annex if a limited distribution is required.)

a. General. (Short summary of the counterintelligence situation during the period.)

b. Espionage.

c. Sabotage.

d. Political.

e. Propaganda and rumors.

f. Miscellaneous.

5. ENEMY CAPABILITIES AND VULNERABILITIES:

a. Enemy capabilities (list).

b. Discussion and analysis. (A *brief* discussion and analysis of the enemy capabilities listed.)

c. Relative probability of adoption. (List in priority of probable adoption of enemy courses of action.)

d. Vulnerabilities (list).

Acknowledge.

(Signature block)

Annexes: Any intelligence document may be disseminated as an annex to a PERINTREP. Order of battle and prisoner of war interrogation reports are usually disseminated in this manner. Although annexes are a means of disseminating detailed intelligence, avoid unnecessary bulk.

Distribution:

Authentication block

EXAMPLE
PERIODIC INTELLIGENCE REPORT (PERINTREP) CORPS

Copy Nr 26
1st Corps
WHAMBO (CT5221) KOREA
250200 February 19....

PERINTREP NR 89
Period Covered: 240001-242400 February 19.....
References: AMSL 552 KOREA, 1:250,000.
Disposal instructions: Units below division destroy within 48 hours of receipt.

1. GENERAL ENEMY SITUATION: Enemy resistance intensified during our attack. Aggressor launched several counterattacks to include the recapture of * * * at 0700 by a force estimated at 2 rifle battalions supported by 10 tanks and an estimated 1 KT airburst nuclear weapon delivered at 0645 hours at * * *. An attack of battalion strength was defeated in Aggressor's attempt to regain * * *. Defensive construction north of * * * River continues. Extensive mine fields and AT ditches are being constructed along the line * * * where wired-in entrenchments and emplaced antitank weapons already exist. The unidentified tank division vicinity * * * has started to displace to dispersal areas vicinity * * *. Annex A, Enemy Situation. Annex B, Potential Nuclear Targets.

2. ENEMY OPERATIONS DURING PERIOD:

a. Strength and dispositions. See Annex C, Order of Battle.

b. Order of Battle, Annex C.

c. Reserves and reinforcements. Annex C.

d. Air Forces. Fifteen medium bombers attacked our rear area supply installations at 2315. A gas dump at * * * was ignited and 12 vehicles destroyed in a motor park near * * *. Enemy increased air ground support during the afternoon by bombing and strafing in grid squares * * *. A total of 6 attacks were made at very low altitude by 2 of 6 aircraft per attack.

e. Antitank units. Enemy antitank weapons in the * * * and * * * areas were effectively used in conjunction with hastily constructed minefields. Other antitank guns of both 80mm and 105mm caliber were sited in depth along * * * north of * * *.

f. Armored units. Ten tanks supported the attack of 2 battalion strength in recapturing * * *. No other tank action reported during the period. The unidentified tank division vicinity * * * is in the process of moving away by infiltration. Reconnaissance reveals previously located dispersal areas to be still occupied, but the density of vehicles in each area is decreasing steadily. Air reconnaissance revealed numerous single vehicles, including tanks or self-propelled guns moving westward along the route * * * during the period. It is likely that these vehicles are going into new dispersal areas in the vicinity of * * *.

g. Artillery. Light harassing artillery fire was reported near Hill * * * before 1400. During the remainder of the period, the firing increased in this area in support of a counterattack. The greatest number of enemy artillery units are near * * * and * * *.

h. Nuclear Warfare. The high air burst 1 KT nuclear weapon fired at 0645 hours at * * * was delivered by undetermined means. This was the first nuclear weapon delivered in the corps area in the last three days. A potential nuclear target of reinforced battalion strength is developing vicinity * * *. Annex B, Potential Nuclear Targets. Location of nuclear delivery means see Overlay 1 to Annex A.

i. Guerrillas. Minor guerrilla activity was reported. A motor messenger was fired upon at 0500 vicinity * * *. A small unguarded road block was discovered at * * * at 0600.

3. OTHER INTELLIGENCE FACTORS:

a. Enemy identifications. Annex C.

b. Enemy organization and strength/combat efficiency Annex C.

c. Casualties. Annex C.

d. Morale. Annex C.

e. Enemy defenses, minefields, etc. Bridges along Hwy * * * at * * * are reported ready for demolitions. New minefields are located south of * * * PW state that greatly increased mine-laying activity is in progress north of * * * near * * *. Annex A, Overlay 1.

f. Administrative installations and support. A large ammunition dump is reported located in the woods east of * * * and the 12th Rifle Division rear echelon installations are in * * * according to PW.

Civilians state a large gasoline dump is in the forest north of * * * and that a mine dump is located at * * *.

g. Weather. Annex D.

4. COUNTERINTELLIGENCE:

a. No marked change in the counterintelligence situation.

b. Espionage. An Aggressor agent was captured at * * *. The agent confessed that her mission was to locate nuclear warhead storage sites.

c. Sabotage. Censorship of civilian mail reveals strong subversive elements among transportation workers in the city of * * * and contemplated sabotage of rail facilities here.

d. Political activity. Annex E, Political Situation.

e. Propaganda and rumors. Aggressor fired about 100 shells containing propaganda leaflets into * * * at 1920 hours. The leaflets stressed the futility of attacking * * * in view of Aggressor's capabilities, and promised safe passage of lines for all who would surrender.

5. ENEMY CAPABILITIES AND VULNERABILITIES:

a. Enumeration. Aggressor can—

(1) Continue to delay on successive positions between present line of contact and * * * line with estimated 3 motorized rifle divisions supported by 25 artillery battalions, 7 battalions of 120mm mortar and 4 antitank battalions.

* * * * * * *

(6) Employ within the army area 5 to 20 nuclear weapons per month with probable yields of 50 KT or less, employing all available delivery means.

b. Analysis and discussion.

(1) Continued delay by Aggressor on successive positions is indicated by following:

* * * * * * *

c. Relative probability of adoption. Continue to delay on successive positions between present line of contact and * * * line reinforced by all available reserves, using all available artillery, air, and nuclear weapons, and continuing harassing guerrilla operations in our rear areas.

d. Vulnerabilities.

(1) West flank from * * * to * * * is open to envelopment.

* * * * * * *

Acknowledge.

PAUL
Maj Gen

Annexes: A—Enemy Situation with Overlay 1 (omitted)
   B—Potential Nuclear Targets (omitted)
   C—Order of Battle (omitted)
   D—Weather (omitted)
   E—Political Situation (omitted)
Distribution: A
OFFICIAL:
 /s/ William
    WILLIAM
    G2

APPENDIX XIII

ANALYSIS OF AREA OF OPERATIONS

The format for an analysis of area of operations is given below.

Heading

ANALYSIS OF AREA OF OPERATIONS NR _____
Reference:
1. PURPOSE AND LIMITING CONSIDERATIONS:
    a. Purpose.
    b. Limiting considerations.
2. GENERAL DESCRIPTION OF THE AREA:
    a. Climatic or weather conditions.
    b. Terrain.
        (1) Relief and drainage system.
        (2) Vegetation.
        (3) Surface materials.
        (4) Manmade features.
    c. Additional characteristics.
3. MILITARY ASPECTS OF THE AREA:
    a. Tactical aspects.
        (1) Observation and fire.
        (2) Concealment and cover.
        (3) Obstacles.
        (4) Key terrain features.
        (5) Avenues of approach.
    b. Administrative support aspects.
        (1) Personnel management.
        (2) Logistics.
        (3) Civil affairs.
4. EFFECTS OF CHARACTERISTICS OF THE AREA:
    a. Effect on enemy courses of action.
    b. Effect on our courses of action.

SIGNATURE BLOCK

Annexes:

EXPLANATION

The exploded example of an analysis of area of operations shown in figures 36A to 36F explains many of the factors that must

Classification is centered at the top and bottom of each page. For training documents, classification is indicated in this manner.

Analyses are numbered successively throughout the calendar year.

References list maps, charts, or other documents required to understand the analysis. References to maps include the country or geographical area and/or map series number, edition (if required), scale, and map sheet name and number.

The time zone, if required, is listed here. In addition, all date-time groups have a suffix to identify further the time zone, if required.

Paragraph 2 is a listing of pertinent facts for use as a basis for the succeeding paragraphs.

Paragraph 2a lists or refers to other documents containing, for the period under study, meteorological conditions, to include precipitation, fog, cloud conditions, temperature, relative humidity, surface winds, effective winds (or winds aloft), atmospheric pressure, light data to include moon phases, moonrise and moonset, and other geodetic data as appropriate. When appropriate, include magnetic phenomena.

(Classification)

Copy Nr 2
1st Corps
BARDOI (187438), NESHUMA
111200 June 19
SB 2

ANALYSIS OF AREA OF OPERATIONS NR 7

Reference: Map, NESHUMA, 1:100,000, BRIGITA.

1. PURPOSE AND OTHER LIMITING CONSIDERATIONS

   a. Purpose. To analyze the area within the corps zone from vicinity WYLA (2157) northwest to and including the POTAPAWI Canal.

   b. Mission. 1st Corps attack 140430 June; seize high ground 2140-2857; destroy enemy in zone; deny area south of POTAPAWI Canal to the enemy; protect army east flank.

2. GENERAL DESCRIPTION OF THE AREA

   a. Climatic or weather conditions.

      (1) Climate. (Annex A, Climatic Summary.)

      (2) Weather forecast, 12 June--15 June.

         (a) Precipitation. None predicted.

         (b) Fog. None predicted.

         (c) Temperature. From 72° to 85°F.

         (d) Wind. Surface winds from the south 7 to 9 miles per hour. Mean effective wind for yields of tactical interest about 15 knots from the south.

(Classification)

Copy number assigned by issuing headquarters official designation of unit. Physical location of command post by coordinates, state, or country.

Date-time group when the analysis is signed.

Message reference number—used when the analysis is distributed *outside* the headquarters for the purpose of acknowledgement in the clear. All appended material to the analysis having the same distribution bears the same reference number.

Paragraph 1a states the exact limits of the area being studied.

Paragraph 1b states the mission and any other limiting considerations such as time limitations, the commander's plan of action and enemy capabilities.

(Classification)

(Analysis of Area of Op Nr 7--1st Corps)

      (e) Cloudiness. None predicted.

      (f) Atmospheric pressure. Average about 980 millibars.

      (g) Moon. New moon: 19 June.

      (h) Light data.

DATE	BMNT	BMCT	EENT	EENT	MOONRISE	MOONSET
13 June	0329	0440	1933	2038	2024	0608
*	*	*	*	*	*	*
16 June	0332	0446	1939	2037	2137	0901

   b. Terrain.

      (1) Relief and drainage systems. (Annex B, Relief Overlay.) Area is drained by the ISHO River on the east and northeast and by the ZOSHA River on the south and southwest. The ridge from Hill 406 (1449) to ROTZ (2254) generally bisects the area. The major spurs of this ridge run generally east and west. The terrain is generally rolling with a series of sharply rising tablelands. The KILRA, ISHO, and ZOSHA Rivers and the POTAPAWI Canal are unfordable. The ISHO River north of BRIGITA averages 30 meters wide and 2 meters deep. The ZOSHA River averages 15 meters wide and 2 meters deep. The POTAPAWI Canal has, steep banks about 3 meters deep and is about 18 to 22 meters wide at the top of the banks. All other rivers and streams are fordable, varying from 1 to 6 meters wide and about 14 inches deep.

Describe configuration of the ground including slopes for personnel and vehicles and critical relief for equipment dependent on line of site. Configuration and conditions of streams, including depth, slope, and condition of banks and bottom, and location of crossing sites. Named localities are located by grid coordinates the first time they appear in the analysis. Grid coordinates are repeated only if required for ease of reference.

Paragraph 2b. Makes maximum use of special colored maps or overlays. Under each characteristic include facts to assist in *subsequent* determination of the effects of the characteristic on the use of nuclear weapons, chemical and biological agents, important devices and equipment used in implementing courses of action. (Do not include here the interpretation of these effects on friendly or enemy possible courses of action.)

(Continued on next page)

(Classification)

Figure 36A. Example of a written analysis of the area of operations.

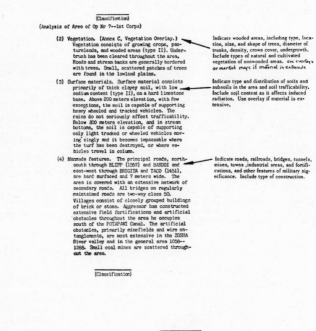

(Classification)
(Analysis of Area of Op Nr 7--1st Corps)

(2) Vegetation. (Annex C, Vegetation Overlay.) Vegetation consists of growing crops, pasturelands, and wooded areas (type II). Underbrush has been cleared throughout the area. Roads and stream banks are generally bordered with trees. Small, scattered patches of trees are found in the lowland plains.

Indicate wooded areas, including type, location, size, and shape of trees, diameter of trunks, density, crown cover, undergrowth. Include types of natural and cultivated vegetation of nonwooded areas. *Use overlays or marked maps if material is extensive*

(3) Surface materials. Surface material consists primarily of thick clayey soil, with low sodium content (type II), on a hard limestone base. Above 200 meters elevation, with few exceptions, the soil is capable of supporting heavy wheeled and tracked vehicles. The rains do not seriously affect trafficability. Below 200 meters elevation, and in stream bottoms, the soil is capable of supporting only light tracked or wheeled vehicles moving singly and it becomes impassable where the turf has been destroyed, or where vehicles travel in column.

Indicate type and distribution of soils and subsoils in the area and soil trafficability. Include soil content as it affects induced radiation. Use overlay if material is extensive.

(4) Manmade features. The principal roads, north-south through BLIPP (1557) and BARDOI and east-west through BRIGITA and TACO (1451), are hard surfaced and 7 meters wide. The area is covered with an extensive network of secondary roads. All bridges on regularly maintained roads are two-way class 50. Villages consist of closely grouped buildings of brick or stone. Aggressor has constructed extensive field fortifications and artificial obstacles throughout the area he occupies south of the POTAPANI Canal. The artificial obstacles, primarily minefields and wire entanglements, are most extensive in the ZOSRA River valley and in the general area 1058--1388. Small coal mines are scattered throughout the area.

Indicate roads, railroads, bridges, tunnels, mines, towns, industrial areas, and fortifications, and other features of military significance. Include type of construction.

(Classification)

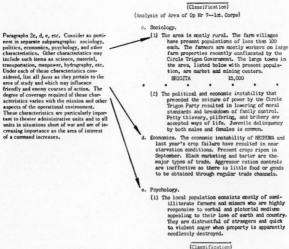

(Classification)
(Analysis of Area of Op Nr 7--1st, Corps)

Paragraphs 2c, d, e, etc. Consider as pertinent in separate subparagraphs: sociology, politics, economics, psychology, and other characteristics. Other characteristics may include such items as science, materiel, transportation, manpower, hydrography, etc. Under each of these characteristics considered, list all *facts* as they pertain to the area of study and which may influence friendly and enemy courses of action. The degree of coverage required of these characteristics varies with the mission and other aspects of the operational environment. These characteristics are particularly important to theater administrative units and to all units in situations short of war and are of increasing importance as the area of interest of a command increases.

c. Sociology.

(1) The area is mostly rural. The farm villages have present populations of less than 100 each. The farmers are mostly workers on large farm properties recently confiscated by the Circle Trigon Government. The large towns in the area, listed below with present population, are market and mining centers.

BRIGITA   15,000

.   .   .   .

(2) The political and economic instability that preceded the seizure of power by the Circle Trigon Party resulted in lowering of moral standards and breakdown of family control. Petty thievery, pilfering, and bribery are accepted ways of life. Juvenile delinquency by both males and females is common.

d. Economics. The economic instability of NESHUMA and last year's crop failure have resulted in near starvation conditions. Present crops ripen in September. Black marketing and barter are the major types of trade. Aggressor ration controls are ineffective as there is little food or goods to be obtained through regular trade channels.

e. Psychology.

(1) The local population consists mostly of semi-illiterate farmers and miners who are highly responsive to verbal and pictorial medium appealing to their love of earth and country. They are distrustful of strangers and quick to violent anger when property is apparently needlessly destroyed.

(Continued on next page)

(Classification)

Figure 36B. Example of a written analysis of the area of operations (cont.).

(Classification)
(Analysis of Area of Op Nr 7--1st Corps)

    (2) Except for a fanatic core of Circle Trigon officials, the local population is hostile to the Circle Trigon regime. This hatred has been fed by the ruthless land confiscation of the regime and the civilian labor impressment policies of the Aggressor forces. The local population expects the UN forces to restore farm property immediately to their original owners.

3. MILITARY ASPECTS OF THE AREA.
  a. Tactical aspects.
    (1) Observation and fire.
      (a) Weather conditions. Weather permits good air and ground observation. Continued dry weather will increase dust clouds caused by nuclear weapons and reduce observation for a significant period in nuclear target areas. Weather favors our use of smoke, but not Aggressor's use of smoke.

      (b) Relief. From the Aggressor-held high ground, observation over approaches into his position is excellent. The Aggressor-held hills west of the KILRA and ISHO Rivers dominate the western part of the area. High ground vicinity Hill 408 (1342) gives Aggressor excellent observation to the southwest, west, and north. The corps objective, with the spur extending south, gives Aggressor excellent observation over all approaches leading directly to it.

(Classification)

Indicate graphically or describe the influence of weather, relief, vegetation, surface materials, manmade features, and other pertinent characteristics. Effects of and on nuclear fires, chemical agents, etc, are included as are any marked effects on surveillance devices, equipment based on line of sight, and fire delivery means. Effects on fire includes effects on delivery means, fields of fire, and effectiveness of fires. Observation and fire is of concern to administrative support units as it influences rear area security considerations.

Paragraph 3. Analyze the facts in the previous paragraph to determine their influence on factors affecting tactical and administrative support activities that are considered in the development of specific courses of action. The extent of the analysis depends on the mission, the means available to accomplish the mission, and the possible means the enemy can use to prevent the accomplishment of the mission. In considering the factors under each aspect, include the effects, as appropriate, of and on nuclear fires, chemical and biological agents, and important devices and equipment used in implementing courses of action.

Paragraph 3a. Consider the effect that the area will have on observation, fire, concealment and cover, and obstacles; and determine key terrain features and avenues of approach.

(Classification)
(Analysis of Area of Op Nr 7--1st Corps)

Fields of fire for flat-trajectory weapons are generally short and good, and excellent in valley bottoms and from the military crests of open hill tops. The excellent fields of fire on the southern slopes of DANKO Woods ridge and Hill 406 and from the southern slopes of the corps objective favor Aggressor defense. Long-range fields of fire to the north from DANKO Woods ridge favor our attack after we have gained this area. Fields of fire for high-angle weapons are good throughout the area.

      (c) Vegetation. Within wooded areas, fields of fire for flat-trajectory weapons are restricted to trails and roads. Vegetation restricts ground level observation. Forest fire smoke clouds will reduce observation throughout the area.

      (d) Manmade features. Village church steeples are high enough to serve as excellent observation points.

    (2) Concealment and cover.
      (a) Relief. The rolling terrain affords partial cover and concealment from ground observation. The rolling terrain and numerous folds in the ground will provide some protection from thermal effects of nuclear bursts.

(Classification)

Indicate graphically or describe the influence of weather, relief, vegetation, and manmade features. Effects of and on nuclear fires, surveillance devices, chemical and biological agents, etc., are included as appropriate. The discussion is oriented not only on protection of own and enemy forces, but also on other operations to include use of guerrillas, infiltration and counterinfiltration, tactical cover and deception, counterintelligence, armor, and artillery. It is also oriented on site requirements for administrative and tactical installations. Include only marked effects that help in selection of friendly and enemy courses of action.

(Continued on next page)

Figure 36C. Example of a written analysis of the area of operations (cont.).

(Analysis of Area of Op Nr 7--1st Corps)

(b) Vegetation. IVAR Forest (1863) offers
excellent concealment for large
units. Woods throughout the area afford some protection from thermal effects because of thick deciduous cover
being in full leaf.

(c) Manmade features. Buildings in the
area offer some cover from small-arms
fire and shell fragments but do not
protect from blast to any significant
degree.

(3) Obstacles.

(a) Relief. Terrain favors Aggressor use
of persistent toxic chemicals in the
valley forward of his present position. Drainage system consisting of
KILRAY, ISHO, and ZOSHA Rivers and
POTAWI Canal.

(b) Vegetation. Woods, especially the IVAR
Forest, will become obstacles in the
event of blowdown or if set afire and
favor the use of persistent chemicals.
Cultivated areas will limit wheeled
vehicles.

(c) Surface materials. In stream bottoms
and below 200 meters elevation, the
wet soil will magnify the cratering
effects of subsurface nuclear bursts
and will support off-road vehicular
traffic except for movement of single
light vehicles.

Indicate graphically or describe natural
and artificial obstacles and the influence
of relief weather, vegetation, surface
materials, and manmade features.
Effects, as appropriate, of and on nuclear fires, chemical and biological agents
and effects on trafficability and acces-
sibility are included. If of significant
influence, the effect of each obstacle on
possible friendly and enemy courses is
indicated. Obstacles and trafficability
influence site locations for administrative support units.

(Analysis of Area of Op Nr 7--1st Corps)

(d) Manmade features. Extensive artificial
obstacles consisting of minefields
and wire are located on the west
flank and in the area 1355--1657.
This hinders movements and limits use
of avenues of approach in these areas.
Except for BRIGITA, buildings and
villages do not present any significant obstacles even if destroyed by
blast.

(4) Key terrain features.

(a) GRILLVAR Hill mass (2041). This terrain feature controls the avenues of
approach in the western part of the
corps zone. It is key terrain if our
plan of attack calls for a main effort
in that area or if a secondary effort
in that area must progress south of it
to ensure success of the main effort.

(b) Hill 390 (1310) and Hill 421 (1820). If
the enemy attacks before we do and
seizes or controls either or both of
these hill masses, it will prevent, or
at least seriously hinder, the launching of the corps attack.

(c) TNOMYEH-NAOJ Ridge. This ridge controls
the area immediately south of the
POTAPAWI Canal and all the major
crossings over the canal. The mission
cannot be accomplished without seizure of this terrain.

* * * * * * * * *

Key terrain features are based on the
analysis of observation and fire, concealment and cover, obstacles, and the
mission. Any locality or area the seizure, retention, or control of which affords a marked advantage to either force
is considered. The influence of each
key terrain feature listed is discussed
briefly. The discussion is oriented
toward subsequent development of friendly and enemy courses of action. Key
terrain features selected are revised as
required by the commander's decision
and current situation. Key terrain features may be omitted when the enemy has
no capability to seize or control terrain
features which will materially affect the
accomplishment of the mission.

(Continued on next page)

Figure 36D. Example of a written analysis of the area of operations (cont.).

Avenues of approach are developed from all the previous analysis of the tactical aspects. Such development does not consider the dispositions of enemy forces. An avenue of approach must afford some facility of movement and room for adequate dispersion for a force large enough to have a significant effect on the outcome of the operation. When either opposing force has available an adequate number of aircraft which can be used to deploy troops and equipment forward of the battle area and significantly affect the accomplishment of the mission, air avenues of approach may be listed. If terrain and weather conditions do not significantly influence choice of flight paths, then air avenues of approach are not listed. Enemy avenues of approach are listed first, followed by a list of our avenues of approach into the enemy battle area. When the opposing forces are not in close contact, or when only security forces are in contact, avenues of approach to the battle area for both forces are listed. Each listing of an avenue of approach is accomplished by a brief discussion to provide a basis for subsequent development of possible courses of action by either force. For administrative support units, the discussion of avenues of approach is based on rear area security requirements.

Personnel management is of particular importance when weather and terrain conditions are severe; when the area of operations has a significant population and potential labor forces, and when political and economic conditions are unsettled.

(Classification)

(Analysis of Area of Op Nr 7--1st Corps)

    (5) Avenues of approach.

      (a) Available to Aggressor into our position.

        1. Axis IRVE (2356)--OLIRI (1632)--Hill 390. This approach is wide enough for at least two regiments with adequate dispersion. It leads almost directly to a key terrain feature, crosses few obstacles, and has good trafficability and a fair road net.

             * * * * *

      (b) Available to us into Aggressor's position.

        1. Axis Hill 398 (1138)--ALEXO (2042)--TNOMYEH-NAOJ Ridge. This approach is wide enough for at least one infantry division with adequate dispersion. It is a valley approach until ALEXO is reached. The valley floor in the vicinity of ALEXO is partially blocked with minefields. When ALEXO is reached, high ground is retained all the way to the corps objective. The road net is excellent and there are no trafficability problems.

             * * * * *

    b. Administrative support aspects.

      (1) Personnel. Sociological characteristics adversely affect discipline, law and order, utilization of civilian labor, and security of installations.

      (2) Logistics. Sociological characteristics adversely affect security of supply installations. Economic characteristics may impose additional logistical burdens. Mines in the area may be sources of construction equipment and materiel.

(Classification)

Paragraph 3b analyzes the facts listed in paragraph 2 and the subconclusions developed under tactical aspects. Indicate those facts and subconclusions which significantly affect administrative support activities influencing choices of possible courses of action by either force or by requiring special activities to ensure adequate support. Omit any activity that is not significantly influenced.

Logistics is of particular importance when weather and terrain conditions are severe, when the area of operations imposes additional logistical requirements and has significant resources of military value, and political and economic conditions are unsettled. Coverage is particularly detailed for those commands accomplishing their mission by logistical support of other units.

Civil affairs is of particular importance in situations short of war, limited war, occupation operations, and when extensive civil affairs responsibilities have been assigned to the command. It is particularly important to tactical units when the numbers of civilians in the area present control problems and restrict use of firepower. Coverage is detailed for those commands with extensive civil affairs responsibilities.

(Classification)

(Analysis of Area of Op Nr 7--1st Corps)

    (3) Civil affairs. Sociological, economic, and psychological characteristics create problems in control of civilians to prevent interference with operations and to maintain security. Dissemination of instructions to civilians will require special measures.

4. EFFECTS OF THE CHARACTERISTICS OF THE AREA

    a. Effect on enemy courses of action.

      (1) Effect on enemy defense.

        (a) Aggressor-held terrain favors defense in depth to the corps objective with main defenses in the GRILLVAR Hill and TNOMYEH--NAOJ Ridge areas. Aggressor has excellent observation over all avenues of approach and his flanks are protected by the rivers on the east and by the river and artificial obstacles on the west. The best avenues of approach to these area are ***

        (b) The excellent visibility permits Aggressor to make maximum use of his supporting fires.

      (2) Effect on enemy attack.

        (a) Aggressor's best avenue of approach is the axis IRVE--OLIRI--Hill 390.

(Classification)

Paragraph 4 contains the conclusions developed in the previous paragraphs. The conclusions are stated in terms of effects on the general courses of action available to both forces.

List in turn each significant possible enemy course of action such as attack, defense, withdrawal, use of air, armor, nuclear fires, chemical and biological agents, guerrillas, etc. Each listed course of action (using separate subparagraphs) is accompanied by a discussion, to indicate the characteristics of the area favoring or not favoring the course of action. For attack courses of action, indicate the best avenue of approach. For defense courses of action, indicate the best defense areas and, if appropriate, the best avenues of approach leading to the defense areas.

(Continued on next page)

Figure 36E. Example of a written analysis of the area of operations (cont.).

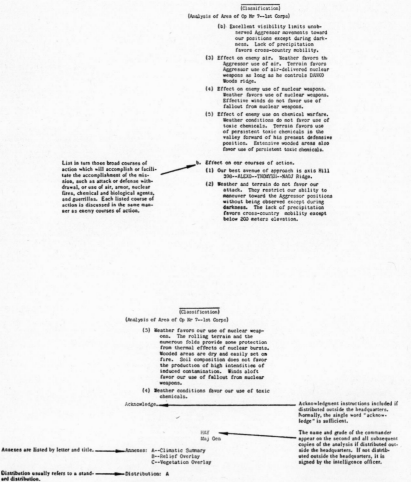

(Classification)

(Analysis of Area of Op Nr 7--1st Corps)

         (b) Excellent visibility limits unobserved Aggressor movements toward our positions except during darkness. Lack of precipitation favors cross-country mobility.

    (3) Effect on enemy air. Weather favors th Aggressor use of air. Terrain favors Aggressor use of air-delivered nuclear weapons as long as he controls DANKO Woods ridge.

    (4) Effect on enemy use of nuclear weapons. Weather favors use of nuclear weapons. Effective winds do not favor use of fallout from nuclear weapons.

    (5) Effect of enemy use on chemical warfare. Weather conditions do not favor use of toxic chemicals. Terrain favors use of persistent toxic chemicals in the valley forward of his present defensive position. Extensive wooded areas also favor use of persistent toxic chemicals.

List in turn those broad courses of action which will accomplish or facilitate the accomplishment of the mission, such as attack or defense withdrawal, or use of air, armor, nuclear fires, chemical and biological agents, and guerrillas. Each listed course of action is discussed in the same manner as enemy courses of action.

  b. Effect on our courses of action.

    (1) Our best avenue of approach is axis Hill 398--ALEXO--TNOMYEH--NAOJ Ridge.

    (2) Weather and terrain do not favor our attack. They restrict our ability to maneuver toward the Aggressor positions without being observed except during darkness. The lack of precipitation favors cross-country mobility except below 200 meters elevation.

(Classification)

(Analysis of Area of Op Nr 7--1st Corps)

    (3) Weather favors our use of nuclear weapons. The rolling terrain and the numerous folds provide some protection from thermal effects of nuclear bursts. Wooded areas are dry and easily set on fire. Soil composition does not favor the production of high intensities of induced contamination. Winds aloft favor our use of fallout from nuclear weapons.

    (4) Weather conditions favor our use of toxic chemicals.

Acknowledge.

Acknowledgment instructions included if distributed outside the headquarters. Normally, the single word "acknowledge" is sufficient.

HAY
Maj Gen

The name and grade of the commander appear on the second and all subsequent copies of the analysis if distributed outside the headquarters. If not distributed outside the headquarters, it is signed by the intelligence officer.

Annexes are listed by letter and title. —— Annexes: A--Climatic Summary
                     B--Relief Overlay
                     C--Vegetation Overlay

Distribution usually refers to a standard distribution. —— Distribution: A

OFFICIAL:
/s/ Seabrook
SEABROOK

This authentication only if the analysis is distributed outside the headquarters.

(Classification)

Figure 36F. Example of a written analysis of the area of operations (cont.).

be considered in preparing an analysis. However, certain features of paragraph 2, *general description of the area* and of paragraph 3, *military aspects of the area,* require further explanation.

CLIMATIC OR WEATHER CONDITIONS. The climatic or weather conditions subparagraph covers only the weather information that has *military importance.* In the remainder of the analysis, this information is interpreted as to its effects. For example, winds at low temperatures are later interpreted in terms of the wind chill factor and the effects on operations such as an attack or defense which must face the prevailing winds, or the use of open or closed storage facilities.

Information on *light conditions* is always included because it influences the selection of courses of action and the conduct of military activities. The beginning of morning nautical twilight *(BMNT)* and the end of evening nautical twilight *(EENT)* are the beginning and end of enough light for limited visibility. At *BMNT,* there is enough light for attacking infantrymen to see each other and also be able to approach an enemy position relatively unobserved. *EENT* is the last time for such light. As a general rule, visibility at *BMNT* is about 400 yards. The beginning of morning civil twilight *(BMCT)* and the end of evening civil twilight *(EECT)* are the beginning and end of enough light for large-scale operations. At about halfway between *BMNT* and *BMCT* (or *EECT* and *EENT*) there is enough light for a ground observer to adjust close-in artillery fires and air strikes. Visibility is also affected by other factors such as weather, position of the observer, terrain relief, and color and reflectivity of clothing, vehicles, and other material. Moon phases, atmospheric conditions, and star brilliance also affect visibility at night. Their influence must be considered because of their effects on friendly and enemy courses of action such as night attacks, patrolling, and other activities.

RELIEF AND DRAINAGE. In studying terrain, drainage and relief lines are the basic elements because they determine the general shape of the ground. A complete study of relief and drainage includes detailed information about slope, configuration, heights, and depth, width, and condition of stream and river banks and bottoms. Various methods for using a map to graphically show these items are described below.

Ridgelining usually consists of using brown lines to show ridge crests. *Streamlining,* using solid blue lines for unfordable streams and broken lines for fordable streams, shows the drainage system at a glance. The more pronounced ridge and drainage lines are emphasized by heavier markings. Stereoscopic examination of an airphoto brings out ridge and stream lines when elevations are not known.

Layer tinting is the coloring of successive elevations on a map. The use of different colors for successive elevations creates a three-dimensional effect. This makes slope and configuration of the ground stand out.

Hill-topping is the coloring, shading, or otherwise emphasizing the tops of hills and noses to show relative elevations. Although hill-topping is easily and quickly done, it is less effective than layer tinting.

Contour shading is the darkening of those parts of an area which are in shadow from an assumed light source. Sharp slopes are generally indicated by darker shading. The result gives the impression of a terrain model. Contour shading is difficult and time consuming, and is best left for mapping units.

In preparing information on *surface* materials, soil maps published by the agricultural services of various countries are particularly valuable. These maps can often be quickly modified into trafficability maps and maps of areas susceptible to high intensities of induced radioactivity. A trafficability map or sketch, based on surface materials information and weather forecasts can be colored or marked to indicate effectively degrees of trafficability.

OBSERVATION AND FIRE. Observation, as discussed in the analysis of the area, is either by eye or by the use of surveillance devices. Observation depends on weather and terrain conditions. The highest terrain usually provides the best observation because most surveillance devices depend on line-of-sight. The availability of aircraft for observation purposes, including carrying surveillance devices, reduces the requirement for high terrain. The use of nuclear weapons affects observation because observation by eye and some types of electronic methods is reduced by the dust and smoke clouds resulting from blast and thermal effects. Other factors that reduce or deny observation include fog, rain, snow, woods, and tall vegetation.

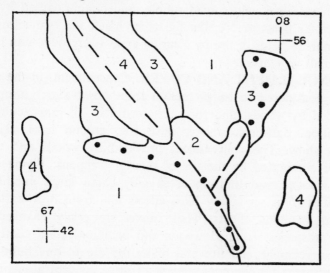

LEGEND

☐1 PASSABLE AT ALL TIMES

☐2 FAIR: PASSABLE WITH DIFFICULTY WHEN WET.

☐3 BAD: IMPASSABLE WHEN WET

☐4 IMPASSABLE AT ALL TIMES

— — — STREAMS IMPASSABLE AT ALL TIMES

● ● ● STREAMS IMPASSABLE UNDER HIGH
        WATER CONDITIONS

NOTE: DIFFERENT COLORS ARE PREFERABLE TO NUMBERING AREAS

Figure 37. Trafficability sketch.

Fire, as used in the analysis, includes the field of fire of the weapon and the characteristics of the delivery weapons influenced by weather and terrain. For example, gusty surface winds reduce the accuracy of free rockets. High, irregular, terrain features may limit fields of fire—the area that can be covered effectively with fire from given positions. Although observation is essential for effective control of fire, the best observation does not always guarantee the best field of fire. An ideal field of fire for flat-trajectory weapons is an open area in which the enemy can be seen and on which he has no protection from the fire. Fields of fire can be quickly changed by the use of nuclear weapons. Tree blow-down, widespread rubble, and craters caused by blast can reduce fields of fire. On the other hand, use of nuclear fires can improve fields of fire by clearing areas overgrown with bushes and small vegetation.

CONCEALMENT AND COVER. Concealment, in the analysis, is considered to be protection from observation. It may be provided by woods, underbrush, snowdrifts, tall grass, cultivated vegetation, darkness, smoke, dust, fog, ground haze, rain, or falling snow. The concealment provided by woods and forests can be eliminated by the use of nuclear weapons. Flying debris from wooded and built-up areas may cause large numbers of casualties from secondary blast effects and from fires started by nuclear weapons effects. These areas are easily changed into major obstacles. Isolated woods and communication centers attract surveillance and fire and make the use of any built-up or wooded areas for the concealment of large concentrations a possible vulnerability. Smoke and dust clouds and fire resulting from use of nuclear weapons may create temporary concealment by restricting observation. Darkness provides concealment but entails the risk of dazzle from nuclear detonations.

Cover is protection from the effects of enemy fires. Terrain features providing cover include ditches, quarries, caves, river banks, folds in the ground, shell craters, buildings, walls, embankments, and cuts. Areas which provide protection against non-nuclear weapons do not necessarily protect against nuclear weapons effects. Unless the forward slopes of a terrain mass are very steep, blast may wound personnel and damage materiel on the reverse slope because the blast wave follows the surface of all but the most rugged terrain. However, irregular terrain does provide some cover from thermal effects. Foxholes, bunkers, and tunnels offer the simplest forms of effective cover.

Concealment and cover are desirable for both the attack and the defense. Troops moving under the concealment of woods, fog, or a moonless night, are better able to achieve surprise. If

troops can move protected from enemy fire by ditches, embankments, or walls the attack will be more effective. A defender seeks
an area which has cover and concealment for the defending
units and does not offer the enemy covered approaches. Cover
and concealment are also sought during troop movements. Routes
with good cover and concealment reduce the vulnerability of a
moving force to detection and to destruction by fire.

OBSTACLES. An obstacle is any natural or artificial terrain
feature which stops or impedes military movement. Natural obstacles include rivers, canals, lakes, swamps, steep slopes, dense
woods, deserts, mountains, and cities. Artificial obstacles are
works of construction and destruction to stop or slow military
movement. They include minefields, craters, anti-tank ditches,
roadblocks, areas deliberately flooded, areas contaminated with
chemical and biological agents or residual nuclear radiation, and
tree blow-down caused by nuclear fires. Obstacles can be quickly
created, strengthened, weakened, or eliminated by nuclear detonations. For example, obstacles located within an area contaminated
by residual radiation are stronger because of the greater difficulty
of eliminating the obstacle. Minefields can be exploded by blast
effects.

Obstacles, to be fully effective, must be covered by observation and fire. However, even undefended obstacles may force an
attacker into concentrations which are easier to detect and are
suitable for nuclear attack. Obstacles perpendicular to the enemy
direction of attack slow him and may force him into concentrations that usually occur when obstacles have to be crossed, and
hold him for a longer time under the defender's fires. Obstacles
parallel to an axis of advance may give the attacker flank protection. However, parallel obstacles may interfere with movements to the flanks.

KEY TERRAIN FEATURES. A key terrain feature is any
locality or area whose *seizure* or *control* affords a marked advantage to either opposing force. Key terrain features are selected
to indicate areas and localities whose seizure or control must be
considered in formulating and selecting courses of action. For
example, a bridge over an unfordable river may give access to
the opposite shore without requiring an assault crossing. Control

of a road or rail center may reduce the enemy's ability to move reserves. A level clearing in rough terrain may be the only available landing field for operations dependent upon the use of helicopters.

Key terrain varies with the level of command. For example, to an army commander a large city may give him a marked advantage as a communications center, but to a division commander the city may only be an obstacle. Obstacles are rarely key terrain features. The high ground dominating a river, rather than the river itself, is usually the key terrain feature. Control of key terrain is not always ensured by seizure and occupation. Occupying key terrain features by relatively large forces may not be desirable. Fixed forces are more easily located and destroyed by nuclear fires. The commander may have to control key terrain without risking destruction of his forces and at the same time keep the enemy from gaining control. Methods of doing this include maneuver, surveillance, and use of fires.

In the offense, key terrain features are usually forward of the edge of the battle area, and are often assigned as objectives. Key terrain features may also be in adjacent sectors if their control is necessary for the continuation of the attack or the accomplishment of the mission. When the mission is to destroy enemy forces, key terrain features are those whose control helps ensure destruction of the enemy. When the mission is to seize or secure an area, key terrain is that which ensures control of the area. Terrain which gives the enemy effective observation along an axis of advance may be key terrain if the enemy *must* be denied its possession or control. Key terrain may be within friendly territory when its control is essential to the success of an offensive operation. For example, if the enemy can attack first and seize or control a terrain feature which prevents or hinders the launching of the friendly attack, then that terrain feature is key terrain because its control gives the enemy a marked advantage.

In the defense, key terrain features are usually within the assigned sector and within or behind the selected defensive area. These features are normally terrain with good observation over avenues of approach to and into the defensive position and terrain permitting covering of obstacles by fire. Communication centers which materially affect command, communications, and the use of reserves may also be critical terrain features.

Key terrain features may also be forward of the defensive area or in adjacent sectors. For example, a terrain feature forward of the edge of the battle area, or in an adjacent sector, which gives the enemy good observation over the defensive positions or communication routes is a key terrain feature when measures must be taken to reduce the enemy advantage. Such measures include moving positions forward to include the feature and use of fire, chemicals, smoke, concealment, and cover to reduce the enemy advantage.

AVENUES OF APPROACH. Avenues of approach are relatively easy routes for a force to reach an objective or key terrain. An avenue of approach must provide some ease of movement and enough width for dispersion of a force large enough to influence seriously the outcome of the operation. The division G2 usually considers avenues of approach that are wide enough for at least a regiment or a battle group or a combat command. The corps and higher G2 usually consider avenues of approach adequate for at least a division. In determining the width for dispersion, consideration is given to deployment patterns, means of movement, and the area required for maneuver to prevent presenting lucrative targets for nuclear fires.

A valley avenue of approach provides some cover and concealment from enemy direct fire and observation. A valley approach includes the slopes of the ridges and the military crests as well as the valley floor. Control of the military crests on each side of the valley is essential. In evaluating the use of a deep valley approach, the possible intensification of nuclear effects and resulting greater casualties on the valley floor are considered. At times, the best axis of advance may be along the slopes below the military crest of the ridge rather than along the valley floor. The use of a ridge approach depends upon the width and shape of the ridge, the size and deployment of the units involved, and the distance to and height of adjacent ridges. A ridge approach usually puts the axis of advance along good observation but there may be little protection from enemy fire falling on the ridge. The best axis of advance in a ridge approach is often slightly below the topographical crest, with sufficient force on the crest to control it.

An *air avenue of approach* is a route which provides a suitable flight path for a particular number of aircraft to reach a drop or landing zone. To be considered an air avenue of approach, a flight path must afford some ease of movement for a force large enough to influence the operation significantly. In selecting air avenues of approach the most important considerations are enough air space for rapid movement to landing or drop zones, ground observation, easily recognized terrain features, terrain corridors, and length of the flight path. In selecting avenues of approach for helicopter operations, the major concern is concealment. Routes selected should provide defilade and be easy to follow in order to make low altitude navigation easy. Ridgelines should be crossed as infrequently as possible in order to minimize radar detection. Steep defiles or canyons are avoided because any appreciable amount of surface winds may cause downdrafts and momentary loss of control. Heavily forested and swampy areas are good routes because they reduce the opportunity of ground troops to see, or take under fire, the helicopters passing overhead at tree top level. Low altitude operations over heavy woods distort aircraft noise and decrease the distance at which it can be heard. It also makes it harder for ground observers to locate the direction of the noise. Aviation officers assist in evaluating the effect of air density, altitude, and visibility on selected air avenues of approach.

INFLUENCE OF WEATHER ON ARMY OPERATIONS

EFFECTS ON PERSONNEL

Weather directly affects the physical well being and emotional state of personnel. Heat exhaustion, frost-bite, snow blindness, and mountain sickness are caused by weather conditions. Weather conditions influence metabolism, physical activity, mental state, and level of resistance to many diseases. Many diseases, such as colds and pneumonia, have a seasonal pattern of occurrence. Prolonged exposure to extremes of temperature and humidity, heavy or prolonged precipitation, high winds, and other harassing weather increases the physical and mental strain on personnel. This adversely affects physical, mental, and emotional conditions and lowers morale and efficiency. The spread of communicable diseases is also affected by weather through influence on the distribution of disease-causing and disease-carrying agents.

EFFECTS ON EQUIPMENT AND SUPPLIES

Precipitation or high humidity may cause rotting or mildewing of rubber, leather, cloth, and rope. Humid conditions with high temperatures cause rapid deterioration of some types of electrical insulating material and corrosion of exposed metal such as small arms and artillery pieces. Materials such as wood, paper, and leather are affected by very high or low humidity. Others such as sugar, tobacco, and glue lose desirable properties above certain degrees of humidity. Many products such as food, medicine, film, and photographic chemicals require special handling in areas where there is very high or low temperature humidity. High winds may damage or destroy many types of unprotected equipment. Blowing sand and dust may damage painted surfaces and equipment such as engines and weapons.

179

EFFECTS ON NATURAL FEATURES

Soil trafficability is affected by precipitation, air and soil temperature, wind, and humidity. The amount of precipitation, coupled with the runoff factor and, at times, with the amount of thaw of snow and ice, controls stream levels and may produce floods. Temperature controls freeze and thaw of snow and ice and the times of winter freezes and spring breakups of ice on bodies of water. Snow cover affects the ability of personnel and vehicles to cross terrain and also affects concealment.

EFFECTS ON MANMADE FEATURES

Lines of communication, such as railways and highways, may be seriously affected by heavy accumulations of snow, by heavy or prolonged precipitation, and by frost action in the soil. Wire communications may be affected by heavy accumulations of snow, formation of ice on wires, strong wind, and frost action in the soil. Buildings and other installations may be affected as follows: heavy accumulations of snow may collapse roofs, high winds, tornadoes, hurricanes, or severe thunderstorms may damage or destroy structures; frost action may damage surfaced runways; hail may break glass, plexiglass, and similar materials; high temperatures may be injurious to paint; and heavy or prolonged rains may weaken foundations and flood subsurface and other installations in low-lying areas.

INFLUENCES ON TACTICAL ACTIVITIES

In intelligence operations, visual observation is hindered by fog, smoke, dust, haze, and precipitation. Visual observation from the air is reduced or prevented by clouds between the observer and the object or areas observed. These factors also apply to aerial photography. In addition, dense clouds may reduce illumination to a point where photography is difficult or impossible. However, a high, thin layer of cloud may make photoreconnaissance easier by reducing ground shadows. Reflection of sunlight from a snow surface may make clear photography difficult.

The effectiveness of listening posts is decreased by thunder, heavy precipitation, high winds, and other conditions which decrease audibility. Sound ranging operations are affected by changes in weather factors, such as temperature, humidity, and wind. Radar is affected by vertical distribution of temperature and moisture in the atmosphere. Clouds and precipitation also influence radar by producing "clutter" which obscures echoes. Wire communciations are affected by electrical discharges in the atmosphere. Excessive ground moisture may reduce the range of field wire circuits using battery-operated telephones. Low frequency radio is affected by electrical discharges. VHF and UHF radio is subject to anomalous propagation resulting from certain moisture and temperature distributions. Messengers are affected by many weather factors, and their ability to move is also subject to weather effects.

Visual communication is reduced by fog, clouds, dust, haze, and precipitation.

A great variety of activities related to strengthening defensive positions, facilitating movement, and obstructing enemy movement are performed by tactical forces. These activities include construction of emplacements and fortifications, mine-laying, and construction of roads, airstrips, and other such facilities. Weather affects the speed with which such tasks can be completed and may provide concealment for forces carrying out such tasks near the enemy. Emplacements must be designed to withstand the weather. Alternate freezes and thaws of the soil prevent using materials which peel, scale, or crack. Prolonged or heavy rainfall softens the ground so that special foundations, bracing, and drainage are necessary to prevent cave-ins and flooding. Heavy rains or severe freezes slow or stop excavation work. Rains may make mine-laying operations easier by softening the ground. Severe freezes may make digging difficult, and increase the time required for laying minefields. Concealment of mines is difficult after a snowfall. However, falling snow quickly obliterates tracks and signs of digging. The amount of rainfall affects plans for foundations and drainage systems for roads, airfields, and similar installations. In addition, weather during actual construction influences methods used and time required for completion of work.

In the movement of personnel, equipment, and supplies, movement by air is affected by clouds, visibility, temperature, and surface winds at terminals, and by clouds, visibility, temperature, wind turbulence, icing, and other hazards occurring over routes. Surface movement is affected by trafficability, conditions of line-of-communication features, and visibility. Each is subject to the effects of weather conditions.

INFLUENCE ON WEAPONS

Weather influences the use of weapons by affecting delivery capabilities and by influencing the terminal effects of the fires. Artillery fire is affected by powder temperature (as it affects muzzle velocity), wind, air density, and air temperature (as they affect trajectory). In the use of guided missiles, wind affects range, and also may alter initial path. Use of smoke generators depends upon wind direction and speed. Rain and snow decrease the effectiveness of incendiary munitions while strong winds increase their effectiveness. The dissemination of gas clouds of chemical and biological agents is influenced by wind speed and direction and vertical temperature gradients. In addition, the effectiveness of some of these agents is influenced by humidity, temperature, and precipitation.

INFLUENCE ON SPECIAL EQUIPMENT

Clouds and obstructions to vision affect searchlight activities. Low clouds provide a reflecting surface which increases the effectiveness of searchlight illumination. Dense fog, precipitation, or other obstructions to vision, decrease searchlight effectiveness by scattering and diffusing the light. The use of loudspeakers in psychological warfare is affected by any weather element which reduces audibility.

APPENDIX XV

INFLUENCE OF WEATHER AND TERRAIN ON NUCLEAR WEAPON EFFECTS

TEMPERATURE

Temperature has no predictable effect on *blast,* but may affect the target vulnerability because cold causes personnel to seek shelter. Extremely low temperatures may affect the strength of certain metals and plastics by making them more sensitive to blast damage.

Temperature has no significant affect on *thermal* radiation, but may affect target vulnerability. Temperature affects the amount and type of clothing that personnel wear, which in turn directly affects vulnerability of troops to thermal radiation. Troops dressed in winter field uniforms, including gloves and some covering for face and neck, are better protected from flash burns than are troops in normal summer uniforms. Prolonged high temperatures in dry weather may, by dehydration, make target elements more sensitive to thermal radiation.

Temperatures may significantly affect *nuclear* radiation, since relative air density depends on air temperature and barometric pressure. Depending on other circumstances, temperature may possibly be a factor in determining the vulnerability of troops to radiation in that it may affect the type of shelter in the target area. The value of any structure as a shield against nuclear radiation is determined by the amount of material between the source of radiation and the individual. Ordinary frame barracks and tents offer very little protection from nuclear radiation, but heavy logs, earth shelters, and basements of buildings offer substantial protection. Clothing offers no protection against nuclear radiation.

VISIBILITY

Visibility has no effect on blast or nuclear radiation but does affect *thermal* intensities. The greatest thermal effect is achieved

183

on a very clear day. Any haze, mist, or fog reduces thermal effects in proportion to the reduction in visibility. Consequently, a smoke blanket or smoke haze over a target area is a defensive measure.

Visibility also determines the distance to which personnel may be subjected to temporary *dazzle*. Dazzle from a daylight burst does not last more than 5 minutes and generally is not an important factor under daylight conditions. However, even temporary blindness is critical for pilots and drivers. When the eye is focused on the fireball, particularly when optical equipment with light-gathering properties is being used, retinal burns, with some permanent loss of visual acuity, can be caused at great distances. Dazzle is important at night when the pupil of the eye is dilated.

PRECIPITATION

Precipitation has no significant effect on blast pressures above 10 pounds per square inch (psi). Moderate to heavy rains can reduce distances to which lower blast overpressures extend. Precipitation affects thermal radiation only by reducing visibility which affects the distance to which thermal radiation extends. The secondary effects of precipitation in the target area are important. Wet uniforms require much higher thermal intensities for ignition. Personnel may also be expected to cover more of the body and to take shelter. After periods of precipitation buildings, equipment, debris, forests, standing crops, and other normally inflammable elements require higher thermal intensities for ignition, and the spread of fires is unlikely.

Precipitation has no significant effect on initial nuclear radiation. Troops tend to take shelter during inclement weather and thus possibly receive some degree of protection. Precipitation can affect *residual* radiation in two ways. First, if a nuclear weapon is air burst in a heavy rain, the radioactive material can be washed out of the rising cloud and deposited in significant quantities. Such residual hazard is not a normal result of an air burst. Second, after a surface or subsurface burst, with significant radioactivity deposited, heavy rain over the area would tend to wash the contamination from buildings, equipment, and vegetation. This reduces intensities in some areas, and possibly causes high concentrations in drainage systems, low ground, and flat, undrained areas.

WIND

Wind direction and velocity have no significant influence on blast, thermal radiation, or initial nuclear radiation. Wind direction and velocity affect the location of the fallout resulting from surface or subsurface burst of nuclear weapons, since contaminated dirt and debris are deposited downwind. The extent of the contaminated area depends on the direction and velocity of winds between the ground and the altitude to which the nuclear cloud rises. To predict the location and extent of the contaminated area, the average wind speeds and directions at various altitudes from the surface to the maximum nuclear cloud height must be known. Dusty conditions are caused in dry soil after a nuclear burst. Depending on speed and direction, wind may clear the dust and increase or decrease observation and concealment.

HUMIDITY

Humidity has no influence on blast or nuclear radiation. It affects target vulnerability to thermal radiation to some degree as it determines the moisture content and consequent ignition susceptibility. However, this is significant only when very high or very low humidities have prevailed for long periods.

CLOUDS

Cloud cover has no significant influence on blast or initial nuclear radiation. Storm clouds, however, may affect the extent and location of the contaminated area resulting from a surface or underground burst. If a weapon is burst above or in a continuous cloud layer over a target, all or a major portion of the thermal radiation may be eliminated. The amount eliminated depends upon the thickness and continuity of the cloud layer and on the position of the burst.

TERRAIN

Terrain that is gently rolling or flat or open generally maximizes nuclear weapons effects. There is little possibility of personnel or material being shielded by terrain irregularities near ground zero, since the *blast* wave is moving almost vertically near ground zero. At some distances from ground zero, hills can provide partial shelter from blast.

Thermal radiation travels in a straight line. Any terrain feature which casts a shadow effectively shields personnel within that shadow.

Initial *nuclear* radiation also travels in a straight line, and any terrain feature between the point of burst and the individual provides protection. However, nuclear radiation is subject to scatter by the atmosphere and even shielded areas can receive up to approximately 10 percent of the dosage in the open because of this scatter phenomenon.

Deep valleys and ravines give some degree of protection from blast when the axis of the valley or ravine points well away from ground zero. Where the axis of the valley points toward ground zero, there is little or no shielding effect, and blast damage may be increased because of the channelizing of the blast wave. Deep valleys and ravines also offer substantial protection from thermal and initial nuclear radiation to troops, materiel, and buildings.

The influence of *forests or wooded areas* on nuclear weapon effects depends on the amount of overhead cover, density of growth of trees, kinds of trees (coniferous or deciduous), and the amount and condition of tree crowns, undergrowth, and forest floor litter. Trees in leaf offer a high degree of protection from direct thermal radiation if the cover is sufficiently continuous. Nuclear weapons have the capability of starting forest fires over wide areas during dry spells. Protection from initial nuclear radiation is insignificant. Blast may create obstacles because of blown down trees and large numbers of secondary blast injuries may occur among troops occupying a forest.

Buildings offer protection depending on type of construction, flammability, distance from ground zero, and other factors. In general, casualties to troops in buildings are cause by secondary blast effects, such as falling walls, ceilings, and flying window glass. Again, depending on type of construction, distance from ground zero, number and size of openings, and other variables, buildings afford some protection from thermal and initial nuclear radiation.

Field fortifications with sufficient overhead cover effectively protect troops. Use of air-burst weapons against troops in such positions produces some casualties, if embrasures, gun ports, or entrances are open. Otherwise, troops are well protected from flying debris and from thermal effects. Casualties from initial nuclear radiation can be expected from a low air-burst unless the overhead cover is very dense and of great thickness. Fortifications may be collapsed by sufficiently high blast pressures. Troops in foxholes have good protection from nuclear weapon effects. The exact degree of protection depends on the location of the foxhole with respect to the ground zero. Close to ground zero, where a large part of the foxhole is open to thermal radiation, there is little protection. Farther out, where most of the foxhole is shaded from thermal radiation, the nuclear radiation entering the foxhole through atmospheric scatter may be the main cause of casualties. The foxhole offers good protection from the missile effect of blast but high overpressures can collapse foxholes and cause casualties by tossing about the occupants. Foxholes that are covered, even with shelter halves, provide protection from thermal radiation, but nuclear radiation will penetrate any normal foxhole cover.

Surface conditions in the target area are usually not very important. When the ground is level and swampy, or consists of loose sand, digging of foxholes or other field fortifications is difficult or impossible. Consequently, the troops forced to depend on above ground shelters are more vulnerable to nuclear weapons effects, unless materials and time are available for construction of heavy bunkers or revetting. Under certain surface conditions, and at proper height of burst, a nuclear explosion causes the formation of a dust cloud over a large area. Although this dust cloud many contain a little or no radioactivity, visibility is restricted until the cloud has dissipated.

Soil composition and density in a surface or subsurface burst affect damage by ground shock. Propagation of the ground shock wave is poorest in light loamy soils and best in plastic wet clay. The pressures transmitted by such plastic wet clay soils may be up to 50 times greater than those transmitted through sandy clay, which is taken as an average soil type. The nature of the soil or rock affects crater size and may also affect the depth of penetration by air-delivered weapons. Air-burst nuclear weapons may induce radioactivity in otherwise harmless substances in the soil. Sodium and manganese are the most common substances thus affected, although other elements are also affected. These elements become radioactive after the burst and emit a residual radiation called induced radiation. Induced radiation from an air burst nuclear weapon may be tactically significant.

APPENDIX XVI

THE INTELLIGENCE ESTIMATE

The outline format for the written intelligence estimate is given below.

FORMAT

INTELLIGENCE ESTIMATE NR:

Reference:

1. MISSION:
2. THE AREA OF OPERATIONS:
   a. Weather.
      (1) Existing situation.
      (2) Effect on enemy courses of action.
      (3) Effect on our courses of action.
   b. Terrain.
      (1) Existing situation.
      (2) Effect on enemy courses of action.
      (3) Effect on our courses of action.
   c. Other characteristics.
      (1) Existing situation.
      (2) Effect on enemy courses of action.
      (3) Effect on our courses of action.

3. ENEMY SITUATION:
   a. Dispositions.
   b. Composition.
   c. Strength.
      (1) Committed forces.
      (2) Reinforcements.
      (3) Air.
      (4) Nuclear, chemical, and biological warfare.
   d. Recent and present significant activities.
   e. Peculiarities and weaknesses.
      (1) Personnel.
      (2) Intelligence.
      (3) Operations.
      (4) Logistics.
      (5) Civil Affairs.
      (6) Personalities.

189

4. ENEMY CAPABILITIES:
   a. Enumeration.
   b. Analysis and discussion.
5. CONCLUSIONS:
   a. Effects of the area of operations on our courses of action.
   b. Probable courses of action.
   c. Enemy vulnerabilities.

                                                    Signature Block

Annexes:
Distribution:
Authentication:

EXAMPLE

The exploded example of a written intelligence estimate (figs. 38A-38E) explains many of the factors considered in preparing the estimate.

USING THE FORMAT

The following discussion explains other factors that must be considered. This discussion and the explanatory notes in the exploded example provide a full guide in using the format.

BASIS FOR ESTIMATE

The intelligence estimate is based on the mission of the command—either one that is assigned or one that is expected. This mission limits the consideration of the effects of each characteristic of the area of operations. When the mission is to attack, the intelligence estimate does not concern itself with defense. It does, however, consider the security of the command. The principle of *use* is applicable—the intelligence estimate must meet the commander's needs.

ENEMY COMPOSITION

The composition part of the enemy situation paragraph lists all the units, including guerrilla type forces, that can interfere with the accomplishment of the mission. Included are supporting units such as air, nuclear delivery, and electronic warfare, that are in the area or may be used *in time* to support the enemy ground elements. Tactical units also list those enemy units believed to be under control of the opposing comparable command

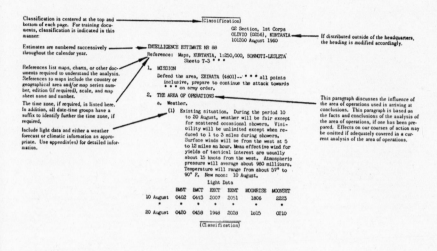

Classification is centered at the top and bottom of each page. For training documents, classification is indicated in this manner:

Estimates are numbered successively throughout the calendar year.

References list maps, charts, or other documents required to understand the analysis. References to maps include the country or geographical area and/or map series number, edition (if required), scale, and map sheet name and number.

The time zone, if required, is listed here. In addition, all date-time groups have a suffix to identify further the time zone, if required.

Include light data and either a weather forecast or climatic information as appropriate. Use appendix(es) for detailed information.

(Classification)

G2 Section, 1st Corps
OLIVIO (0256), KURTANIA
101200 August 1960

If distributed outside of the headquarters, the heading is modified accordingly.

INTELLIGENCE ESTIMATE NR 88

Reference: Maps, KURTANIA, 1:250,000, BONNOTI-LESLETA Sheets T-3 * * *

1. MISSION

    Defend the area, ZEIRATA (4601)-- * * * all points inclusive, prepare to continue the attack towards * * * on army order.

2. THE AREA OF OPERATIONS

    a. Weather.

        (1) Existing situation. During the period 10 to 20 August, weather will be fair except for scattered occasional showers. Visibility will be unlimited except when reduced to 1 to 3 miles during showers. Surface winds will be from the west at 5 to 12 miles an hour. Mean effective wind for yields of tactical interest are usually about 15 knots from the west. Atmospheric pressure will average about 980 millibars. Temperature will range from about 57° to 90° F. New moon: 10 August.

This paragraph discusses the influence of the area of operations used in arriving at conclusions. This paragraph is based on the facts and conclusions of the analysis of the area of operations, if one has been prepared. Effects on our courses of action may be omitted if adequately covered in a current analysis of the area of operations.

Light Data

	BMNT	BMCT	EECT	EENT	MOONRISE	MOONSET
10 August	0402	0443	2007	2051	1806	2223
	*	*	*	*	*	*
20 August	0420	0458	1948	2028	1815	0210

(Classification)

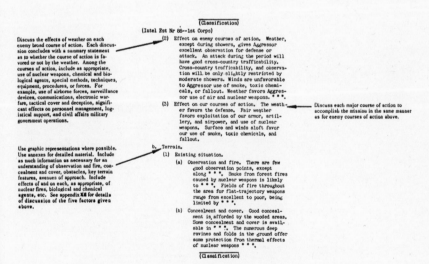

(Classification)

(Intel Est Nr 88--1st Corps)

Discuss the effects of weather on each enemy broad course of action. Each discussion concludes with a summary statement as to whether the course of action is favored or not by the weather. Among the courses of action, include as appropriate, use of nuclear weapons, chemical and biological agents, special methods, techniques, equipment, procedures, or forces. For example, use of airborne forces, surveillance devices, communications, electronic warfare, tactical cover and deception, significant effects on personnel management, logistical support, and civil affairs military government operations.

Use graphic representations where possible. Use annexes for detailed material. Include as much information as necessary for an understanding of observation and fire, concealment and cover, obstacles, key terrain features, avenues of approach. Include effects of and on each, as appropriate, of nuclear fires, biological and chemical agents, etc. See appendix XII for details of discussion of the five factors given above.

        (2) Effect on enemy courses of action. Weather, except during showers, gives Aggressor excellent observation for defense or attack. An attack during the period will have good cross-country trafficability. Cross-country trafficability, and observation will be only slightly restricted by moderate showers. Winds are unfavorable to Aggressor use of smoke, toxic chemicals, or fallout. Weather favors Aggressor use of air and nuclear weapons. * * *.

        (3) Effect on our courses of action. The weather favors the defense. Fair weather favors exploitation of our armor, artillery, and airpower, and use of nuclear weapons. Surface and winds aloft favor our use of smoke, toxic chemicals, and fallout.

    b. Terrain.

        (1) Existing situation.

            (a) Observation and fire. There are few good observation points, except along * * *. Smoke from forest fires caused by nuclear weapons is likely to * * *. Fields of fire throughout the area for flat-trajectory weapons range from excellent to poor, being limited by * * *.

            (b) Concealment and cover. Good concealment is afforded by the wooded areas. Some concealment and cover is available in * * *. The numerous deep ravines and folds in the ground offer some protection from thermal effects of nuclear weapons * * *.

Discuss each major course of action to accomplish the mission in the same manner as for enemy courses of action above.

(Classification)

Figure 38A. Example of a written intelligence estimate.

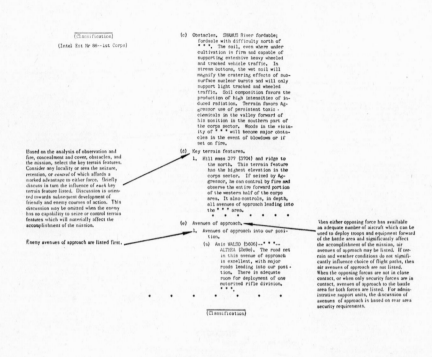

(Classification)

(Intel Est Nr 88--1st Corps)

(c) Obstacles. SHAMUS River fordable; fordable with difficulty north of * * *. The soil, even where under cultivation is firm and capable of supporting extensive heavy wheeled and tracked vehicle traffic. In stream bottoms, the wet soil will magnify the cratering effects of sub-surface nuclear bursts and will only support light tracked and wheeled traffic. Soil composition favors the production of high intensities of in-duced radiation. Terrain favors Ag-gressor use of persistent toxic chemicals in the valley forward of his position in the southern part of the corps sector. Woods in the vicin-ity of * * * will become major obsta-cles in the event of blowdown or if set on fire.

Based on the analysis of observation and fire, concealment and cover, obstacles, and the mission, select the key terrain features. Consider any locality or area the seizure, retention, or control of which affords a marked advantage to either force. Briefly discuss in turn the influence of *each* key terrain feature listed. Discussion is orien-ted towards subsequent development of friendly and enemy courses of action. This discussion may be omitted when the enemy has no capability to seize or control terrain features which will materially affect the accomplishment of the mission.

(d) Key terrain features.

1. Hill mass 377 (3704) and ridge to the north. This terrain feature has the highest elevation in the corps sector. If seized by Ag-gressor, he can control by fire and observe the entire forward portion of the western half of the corps area. It also controls, in depth, all avenues of approach leading into the * * * area.

* * * * * * * *

Enemy avenues of approach are listed first.

(e) Avenues of approach.

1. Avenues of approach into our posi-tion.

(a) Axis WALSO (5606)--* * *-- ALTHEA (2698). The road net in this avenue of approach is excellent, with major roads leading into our posi-tion. There is adequate room for deployment of one motorized rifle division. * * *.

* * * * * * * *

When either opposing force has available an adequate number of aircraft which can be used to deploy troops and equipment forward of the battle area and significantly affect the accomplishment of the mission, air avenues of approach may be listed. If ter-rain and weather conditions do not signifi-cantly influence choice of flight paths, then air avenues of approach are not listed. When the opposing forces are not in close contact, or when only security forces are in contact, avenues of approach to the battle area for both forces are listed. For admin-istrative support units, the discussion of avenues of approach is based on rear area security requirements.

(Classification)

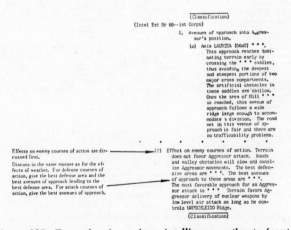

(Classification)

(Intel Est Nr 88--1st Corps)

2. Avenues of approach into Aggres-sor's position.

(a) Axis LAURIEA (56o2) * * *. This approach reaches domi-nating terrain early by crossing the * * * saddles, thus avoiding the deepest and steepest portions of two major cross compartments. The artificial obstacles in these saddles are shallow. Once the area of Hill * * * is reached, this avenue of approach follows a wide ridge large enough to accom-modate a division. The road net in this avenue of ap-proach is fair and there are no trafficability problems.

* * * * * * *

Effects on enemy courses of action are dis-cussed first.

Discuss in the same manner as for the ef-fects of weather. For defense courses of action, give the best defense area and the best avenues of approach leading to the best defense area. For attack courses of action, give the best avenues of approach.

(2) Effect on enemy courses of action. Terrain does not favor Aggressor attack. Woods and valley obstacles will slow and canal-ize Aggressor movements. The best defen-sive areas are * * *. The best avenues of approach to these areas are * * *. The most favorable approach for an Aggres-sor attack is * * * Terrain favors Ag-gressor delivery of nuclear weapons by low level air attack as long as he con-trols UMPSCHLEIDO Ridge.

(Classification)

Figure 38B. Example of a written intelligence estimate (cont.).

[Classification]

(Intel Est Nr 88--1st Corps)

       (3) Effect on our courses of action. The ter-
rain favors the defense in the * * *
The best avenue of approach to this defense area is * * *. The steep slopes of
the * * * are formidable obstacles to
mechanized attack. The broken rolling
country and steep stream valleys within
our position favor defense on successive
positions. Near the corps south boundary
the terrain is relatively open, with no
terrain obstacles between * * *. The
terrain generally favors the use of nuclear weapons. Rubble and blowdown resulting from nuclear blast could make formidable obstacles of cities, towns, and
woods in the zone. The terrain favors
the use of toxic chemicals.

→ Discuss in the same manner as for effects
of terrain on enemy courses of action.

c. Other characteristics.

       (1) Psychological. Aggressor nuclear attacks
of nonmilitary targets have resulted in
bitter hostility by local civilians to
Aggressor forces.

       (2) Effect on enemy courses of action. Atti-
tude of civilians will probably hamper
operations of Aggressor guerrillas in our
sector.

       (3) Effect on own courses of action. Hostile
attitude of civilians toward Aggressor
can be exploited to assist in anti-
guerrilla operations.

[Classification]

The following additional characteristics
are considered, as pertinent, in separate
subparagraphs: sociology, politics, economics, psychology, and other factors.
Other factors may include such items as
science, material, transportation, manpower, and hydrography. They are analyzed
under the same headings as weather and
terrain.

[Classification]

(Intel Est Nr 88--1st Corps)

3. ENEMY SITUATION

  a. Dispositions. Annex A, Situation Overlay.

  b. Composition. Aggressor forces opposing the
corps are estimated to be the 40th and 195th
Rifle Div, and elements of the 40th Rifle Regt,
19th Rifle Div. Aggressor 22d Corps, which is
known to be operating in this area, is believed
to be the controlling headquarters for the 83d,
40th, and 195th Rifle Div. The normal corps
artillery is supporting the divisions in contact. The unidentified mechanized rifle unit
located in the vicinity of * * * is estimated
to be a mechanized rifle regiment and is
believed to be in corps reserve. An estimated 1,200 guerrillas, lightly armed, are
operating in the * * * area. At least one
300-mm gun battalion and 1 ROCKO and 1
MICKY missile battalion and elements of a
howitzer division are known to be in support
of Aggressor 22d Corps. Elements of the
4th Air Army have been supporting Aggressor forces in our sector.

→ Reference may be made to overlay or
enemy situations, maps, or previously
published documents.

List all units, including guerrilla-type
forces, with identifications, that can
affect the accomplishment of the
mission. Included are supporting units
such as air, nuclear delivery, and
electronic warfare. In determining which
enemy units can effect the accomplishment of the mission, consider time and
space factors. Reference may be made to
previously published documents.

  c. Strength.

      (1) Committed forces. 1st Corps is opposed by
approximately 7 rifle regiments and 3
medium tank regiments supported by 14
battalions of artillery, 2 antitank
battalions,, two 150-mm mortar battalions
one 250-mm rocket battalion, one 300-mm
gun battalion, 1 ROCKO battalion, and
1 MICKY battalion. 1st Corps is also
opposed by about 250 guerrillas, lightly
armed.

→ Enemy strength in this subparagraph is
categorized as committed forces, reinforcements, air, and nuclear, chemical,
and biological warfare. The categori-
zation assists in developing enemy
capabilities and vulnerabilities. Air,
nuclear, chemical, or biological warfare
units are omitted, as appropriate, when
the enemy lacks such capabilities to
interfere with the accomplishment of the
mission. The total of the forces listed
cannot exceed, but can equal or be less
than, the total of the forces listed in the
composition subparagraph.

      (2) Reinforcements. Aggressor reinforcements
available for commitment in our zone
are--

         (a) Estimated mechanized regiment located
vicinity of * * *.

→ Reinforcements are those enemy forces
which may or may not be employed
against us depending on our choice of
specific course of action and enemy
plans. Include designation and location.
Omit if there are no reinforcements.

This paragraph gives that information
of the enemy to permit later development
of enemy capabilities and vulnerabilities
and refinement of these capabilities into
specific courses of action and their
relative probability of adoption. In
preparing this paragraph, judgment is
required to isolate the pertinent items
of information.

Committed forces are those enemy ground
units, their immediate reserves, and their
supporting ground fire units, committed
against the friendly unit and whose area of
employment is not expected to change to
counter the specific course of action selected by the friendly commander. Include artillery and other units in position to support
the committed forces with fire and chemical
and biological warfare agents. Specify, as
appropriate, which units can deliver nuclear
fires, chemical agents, etc. Omit if there
are no committed forces.

[Classification]

Figure 38C. Example of a written intelligence estimate (cont.).

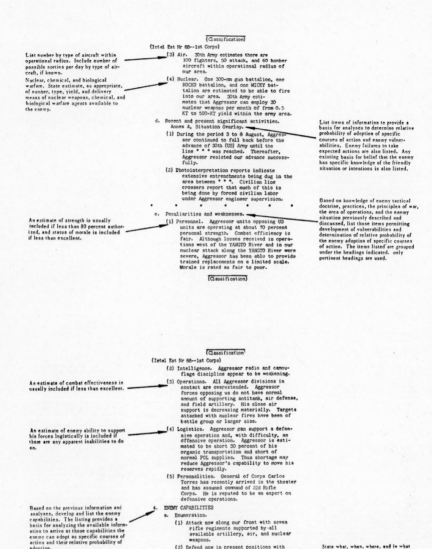

(Classification)

(Intel Est Nr 68--1st Corps)

List number by type of aircraft within operational radius. Include number of possible sorties per day by type of aircraft, if known.

    (3) Air.   30th Army estimates there are 100 fighters, 50 attack, and 60 bomber aircraft within operational radius of our area.

Nuclear, chemical, and biological warfare. State estimate, as appropriate, of number, type, yield, and delivery means of nuclear weapons, chemical, and biological warfare agents available to the enemy.

    (4) Nuclear.   One 300-mm gun battalion, one ROCKO battalion, and one MICKY battalion are estimated to be able to fire into our area.   30th Army estimates that Aggressor can employ 30 nuclear weapons per month of from 0.5 KT to 500-KT yield within the army area.

  d. Recent and present significant activities. Annex A, Situation Overlay.

    (1) During the period 3 to 8 August, Aggressor continued to fall back before the advance of 30th (US) Army until the line * * * was reached. Thereafter, Aggressor resisted our advance successfully.

    (2) Photointerpretation reports indicate extensive entrenchments being dug in the area between * * *. Civilian line crossers report that much of this is being done by forced civilian labor under Aggressor engineer supervision.

    * * * * * * * *

List items of information to provide a basis for analyses to determine relative probability of adoption of specific courses of action and enemy vulnerabilities. Enemy failures to take expected actions are also listed. Any existing basis for belief that the enemy has specific knowledge of the friendly situation or intentions is also listed.

  e. Peculiarities and weaknesses.

An estimate of strength is usually included if less than 80 percent authorized, and status of morale is included if less than excellent.

    (1) Personnel. Aggressor units opposing US units are operating at about 70 percent personal strength. Combat efficiency is fair. Although losses received in operations west of the YANGTO River and in our nuclear attack along the YANGTO River were severe, Aggressor has been able to provide trained replacements on a limited scale. Morale is rated as fair to poor.

Based on knowledge of enemy tactical doctrine, practices, the principles of war, the area of operations, and the enemy situation previously described and discussed, list those items permitting development of vulnerabilities and determination of relative probability of the enemy adoption of specific courses of action. The items listed are grouped under the headings indicated. only pertinent headings are used.

(Classification)

(Classification)

(Intel Est Nr 68--1st Corps)

    (2) Intelligence. Aggressor radio and camouflage discipline appear to be weakening.

An estimate of combat effectiveness is usually included if less than excellent.

    (3) Operations. All Aggressor divisions in contact are overextended. Aggressor forces opposing us do not have normal amount of supporting antitank, air defense, and field artillery. His close air support is decreasing materially. Targets attacked with nuclear fires have been of battle group or larger size.

An estimate of enemy ability to support his forces logistically is included if there are any apparent inabilities to do so.

    (4) Logistics. Aggressor can support a defensive operation and, with difficulty, an offensive operation. Aggressor is estimated to be short 30 percent of his organic transportation and short of normal POL supplies. Thus shortage may reduce Aggressor's capability to move his reserves rapidly.

    (5) Personalities. General of Corps Carlos Torres has recently arrived in the theater and has assumed command of 22d Rifle Corps. He is reputed to be an expert on defensive operations.

  4. ENEMY CAPABILITIES

    a. Enumeration.

Based on the previous information and analyses, develop and list the enemy capabilities. The listing provides a basis for analyzing the available information to arrive at those capabilities the enemy can adopt as specific courses of action and their relative probability of adoption.

    (1) Attack now along our front with seven rifle regiments supported by all available artillery, air, and nuclear weapons.

    (2) Defend now in present positions with seven rifle regiments supported by all available artillery, air, and nuclear weapons.

State what, when, where, and in what strength, for each capability.

(Classification)

Figure 38D. Example of a written intelligence estimate (cont.).

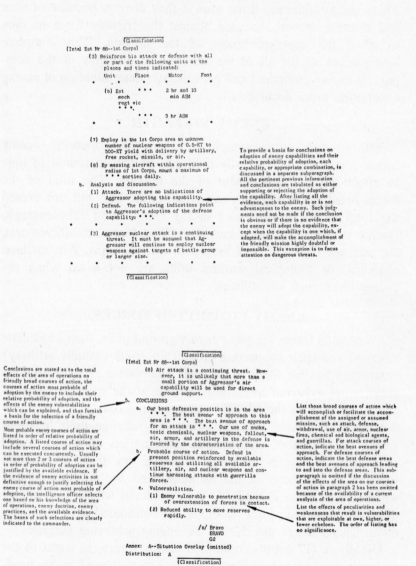

(Classification)

(Intel Est Nr 68--1st Corps)

    (3) Reinforce his attack or defense with all
        or part of the following units at the
        places and times indicated:

Unit	Place	Motor	Foot
(b) Est mech regt vic	* * *	2 hr and 10 min ASM	
	* * *	3 hr ASM	

    (7) Employ in the 1st Corps area an unknown
        number of nuclear weapons of 0.5-KT to
        500-KT yield with delivery by artillery,
        free rocket, missile, or air.

    (8) By massing aircraft within operational
        radius of 1st Corps, mount a maximum of
        * * * sorties daily.

b. Analysis and discussion.

    (1) Attack. There are no indications of
        Aggressor adopting this capability.

    (2) Defend. The following indications point
        to Aggressor's adoption of the defense
        capability: * * *.

    (3) Aggressor nuclear attack is a continuing
        threat. It must be assumed that Ag-
        gressor will continue to employ nuclear
        weapons against targets of battle group
        or larger size.

To provide a basis for conclusions on adoption of enemy capabilities and their relative probability of adoption, each capability, or appropriate combination, is discussed in a separate subparagraph. All the pertinent previous information and conclusions are tabulated as either supporting or rejecting the adoption of the capability. After listing all the evidence, each capability is or is not advantageous to the enemy. Such judgments need not be made if the conclusion is obvious or if there is no evidence that the enemy will adopt the capability, except when the capability is one which, if adopted, will make the accomplishment of the friendly mission highly doubtful or impossible. This exception is to focus attention on dangerous threats.

(Classification)

(Classification)

(Intel Est Nr 68--1st Corps)

    (8) Air attack is a continuing threat. How-
        ever, it is unlikely that more than a
        small portion of Aggressor's air
        capability will be used for direct
        ground support.

Conclusions are stated as to the total effects of the area of operations on friendly broad courses of action, the courses of action most probable of adoption by the enemy to include their relative probability of adoption, and the effects of the enemy vulnerabilities which can be exploited, and thus furnish a basis for the selection of a friendly course of action.

Most probable enemy courses of action are listed in order of relative probability of adoption. A listed course of action may include several courses of action which can be executed concurrently. Usually not more than 2 or 3 courses of action in order of probability of adoption can be justified by the available evidence. If the evidence of enemy activities is not definitive enough to justify selecting the enemy course of action most probable of adoption, the intelligence officer selects one based on his knowledge of the area of operations, enemy doctrine, enemy practices, and the available evidence. The bases of such selections are clearly indicated to the commander.

5. CONCLUSIONS

  a. Our best defensive position is in the area
    * * *. The best avenue of approach to this
    area is * * *. The best avenue of approach
    for an attack is * * *. Our use of smoke,
    toxic chemicals, nuclear weapons, fallout,
    air, armor, and artillery in the defense is
    favored by the characteristics of the area.

  b. Probable course of action. Defend in
    present position reinforced by available
    reserves and utilizing all available ar-
    tillery, air, and nuclear weapons and con-
    tinue harassing attacks with guerrilla
    forces.

  c. Vulnerabilities.

    (1) Enemy vulnerable to penetration because
        of overextension of forces in contact.

    (2) Reduced ability to move reserves
        rapidly.

/s/ Bravo
BRAVO
G2

Annex: A--Situation Overlay (omitted)
Distribution: A

(Classification)

List those broad courses of action which will accomplish or facilitate the accomplishment of the assigned or assumed mission, such as attack, defense, withdrawal, use of air, armor, nuclear fires, chemical and biological agents, and guerrillas. For attack courses of action, indicate the best avenues of approach. For defense courses of action, indicate the best defense areas and the best avenues of approach leading to and into the defense areas. This subparagraph is omitted if the discussion of the effects of the area on our courses of action in paragraph 2 has been omitted because of the availability of a current analysis of the area of operations.

List the effects of peculiarities and weaknesses that result in vulnerabilities that are exploitable at own, higher, or lower echelons. The order of listing has no significance.

Figure 38E. Example of a written intelligence estimate (cont.).

but which are committed outside the zone of the friendly unit. These enemy units are listed even if they cannot, because of time and distance factors, be used against the friendly force in time to affect the accomplishment of the mission. This complete listing accounts for all of the subordinate elements of the comparable enemy command and permits later determination of enemy capabilities more accurately.

ENEMY STRENGTH

The strength subparagraph lists only the opposing enemy forces which can be logically used against the command *in time* to affect the accomplishment of the mission. The total of the forces listed under strength can equal or be less, but not exceed the total of the forces listed in the composition subparagraph. Enemy strength is divided into committed forces, reinforcements, air, nuclear, chemical, and biological warfare units. Air, nuclear, chemical, or biological warfare units are not listed when the enemy lacks such capabilities.

ENEMY COMMITTED FORCES

Committed forces are those enemy ground units, their immediate reserves, and their supporting ground fire units (usually artillery) committed against the friendly unit and whose *area of employment is not expected to change* because of the specific course of action selected by the friendly commander. Committed forces are not necessarily fixed in place—they may change their locations *within* their area of employment. Designation of enemy forces as committed forces depends primarily on their disposition, location at the time of the estimate, and the headquarters at which the estimate is made. If there is doubt whether an enemy unit is a committed force, it should be considered as a reinforcement. This reduces the risk of the enemy achieving surprise.

Usually, a G2 counts committed enemy forces, in terms of the size unit used to oppose that friendly size unit used in his headquarters as a basis for planning and conducting operations. For example, a division G2 usually counts committed forces in terms of battalion size units; a corps G2 in terms of regimental size units, and field army and higher headquarters in terms of divisions. Although the numbers of enemy corps and armies may be mentioned, they are not used as a basis of counting committed forces because their composition is so variable. Where the committed forces, such as guerrillas, do not have a known organization, the strength is given in total numbers.

The determination of committed forces is illustrated in the following example. Figure 39 shows the situation. Our 20th Infantry Division has been stopped by elements of 2 motorized rifle regiments of the Aggressor 11th Motorized Rifle Division. Each of these 2 regiments has 2 rifle battalions in contact and 1 rifle battalion in regimental reserve. A third regiment of this division is in contact with our 72d Infantry Division. About 25 miles in rear of the 11th Motorized Rifle Division and in the area of the 20th Infantry Division objective, 2 motorized rifle regiments of the Aggressor 42d Motorized Rifle Division are preparing field fortifications.

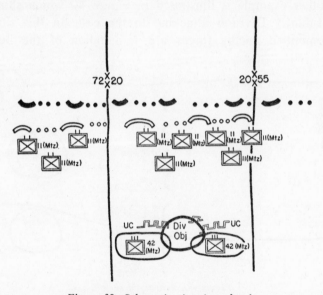

Figure 39. Schematic situation sketch.

The 20th Infantry Division G2 counts only the 4 battalions in contact with his division as committed forces. Regardless of the specific courses of action selected by the 20th Infantry Division commander to continue the advance, the area of commitment of these 4 battalions will not change appreciably, even if they shift companies with their areas. The reserve battalions of the regiments in contact are not committed forces because they are not committed to action. The 2 regiments of the 42d Motorized Rifle Division are not committed forces because enemy plans for their area of commitment, considering their present locations, may depend on the particular courses of action selected by the commanders of the 20th Infantry Division and the adjacent divisions. At this time, the enemy commander is free to commit all or part of them against the 20th Infantry Division or adjacent divisions. The regiment of the 11th Rifle Division in contact with the 72d Infantry Division is mentioned in the *composition* subparagraph. Only the reserve battalion of that regiment is mentioned in the reinforcement part of the *strength* subparagraph because the other 2 battalions are committed outside the zone of the 20th Infantry Division.

Another example is illustrated in Figure 40 which shows the 20th Infantry Division attacking to the east. In this situation, the committed enemy forces are 1 battalion of the 3d Rifle

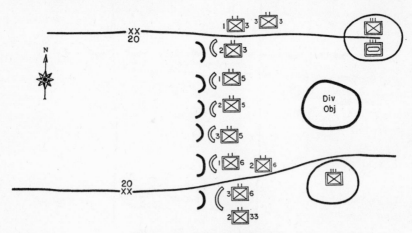

Figure 40. Schematic sketch.

Regiment, 3 battalions of the 5th Rifle Regiment, and 1 battalion of the 6th Rifle Regiment. The 3d Battalion of the 3d Rifle Regiment is from its location, in regimental reserve and has not been committed. Because all battalions of the 5th Rifle Regiment appear to be committed against the 20th Infantry Division, they are committed forces. The 2d Battalion of the 6th Rifle Regiment, according to its location, is the uncommitted reserve of the 6th Rifle Regiment. All other units not mentioned are not committed forces because enemy plans for their area of commitment may be influenced by the courses of action selected by the commanders of the 20th Infantry Division and the adjacent divisions.

ENEMY REINFORCEMENTS

Reinforcements are the other enemy forces—besides committed forces—that can influence the outcome of a particular operation. Reinforcements are those enemy forces whose area of *possible* commitment is influenced by the friendly courses of action selected, and can be committed against the friendly force *in time* to affect the accomplishment of the mission. In the situation shown in figure 39 the 2 regiments of the 42d Rifle Division and the 3 battalions apparently regimental reserves are considered as reinforcements. These units are not committed and can be committed in time to affect the accomplishment of the 20th Infantry Division mission. Although the 2 regiments of the 42d Rifle Division are digging field fortifications in the vicinity of the division objective, the enemy commander can commit them against the 20th Infantry Division at other places *in time* to affect the accomplishment of the division's mission. The enemy can also commit these units against the divisions on the flanks of the 20th Infantry Division.

In the situation shown here in figure 40, the reinforcements are the Aggressor rifle regiment and the tank regiment astride the 20th Infantry Division's north boundary, the rifle regiment below the south boundary, and the 2 uncommitted battalions forward. From their locations and dispositions, it is apparent that these units are the reserves of the 2 divisions and the regiments committed against the 20th Infantry Division. All or some of these reserves can be committed against the 20th Infantry Division *in time* to affect the accomplishment of the division's mission.

Reinforcements are stated in convenient terms that are meaningful to the commander. For example, if the opposing division has a rifle regiment in reserve, this reinforcement is referred to as a *rifle regiment* rather than *3 rifle battalions*. When enemy units, either committed forces or reinforcements are very much understrength, the estimated strength is stated.

The determination of committed forces and reinforcements is not a useless exercise in mental gymnastics for intelligence officers. An understanding of which enemy forces are committed within an area and those which can be maneuvered with greater freedom against the friendly forces is necessary for proper selection of a course of action. This knowledge and understanding enables the commander to mentally war game a course of action better when he analyses opposing courses of action in making an estimate of the situation.

ENEMY AIR CAPABILITY

The enemy air strength is calculated on the basis of the number of enemy aircraft within operational radius, maintenance capabilities, expected losses, the ground tactical situation, and other factors. The supporting tactical air force furnishes intelligence on the number of sorties, by type, which the enemy can be expected to make within the field army area. No attempt is usually made to calculate the number of possible or probable sorties against a subordinate command of the field army or communications zone section. Corps, division, and communications zone section intelligence officers usually quote the estimate furnished by the higher headquarters in stating enemy air capabilities. For example, a corps or division G2 might state *"Thirtieth Army estimates that the enemy can be expected to attack daily within the army area with as many as 150 fighter, 100 attack, and 75 bomber sorties. The enemy can make a maximum of 250 fighter, 300 attack, and 250 bomber sorties daily."*

NUCLEAR, CHEMICAL AND BIOLOGICAL CAPABILITIES

Enemy nuclear, chemical, and biological warfare capabilities are determined primarily on the basis of estimates of numbers and types of weapons and amount and types of agents available, knowledge of enemy doctrine, and past experience. A statement of these capabilities includes, if known, the amount and type of weapons available to deliver chemical and biological munitions. Estimates of enemy nuclear, chemical, and biological warfare capabilities are usually prepared at field army and higher headquarters. Units below field army usually cannot collect the information to make such estimates, and therefore use the estimates of the higher headquarters, modifying them with any available information. As with the enemy air capability, it is rarely possible to estimate the proportion that will be used against a division or corps or a section of the communications zone. It is also not feasible to estimate the number of nuclear weapons the enemy is capable of using within a period as short as 1 day. The period selected depends on the available information and past experience.

ENEMY PECULIARITIES AND WEAKNESSES

The peculiarities and weaknesses subparagraph lists and briefly discusses each to bring out the extent to which vulnerabilities exist and the effect on the selection of friendly broad courses of action. For example, if the enemy has an open flank, it is stated in the *operations* part of the subparagraph and the extent to which it is an exploitable vulnerability is discussed briefly. If enemy reserves are small, not motorized, and far from the open flank, the vulnerability may be great. The G2 might state it as, *"The enemy north flank is open. Available reserves, now not motorized and 8 hours marching distance away, can only extend this flank for about 2,000 yards. Positions to extend the flank have not been prepared. The enemy is vulnerable to a flank attack."* If the enemy reserves are large and motorized and in position to extend the flank or to counterattack an enveloping force, the vulnerability is probably insignificant. The G2 might then state it as, *"The enemy north flank is open. However, available motorized reserves are adequate either to extend this flank quickly beyond our zone, or to counterattack an enveloping force. Positions to block an envelopment have been prepared as shown on the enemy situation map."* In the first case, the enemy's vulnerability to a flank attack is carried forward to the *conclusions* paragraph of the intelligence estimate. In the second case, the open flank apparently is not a vulnerability, and is not carried any further.

Another example, if guerrilla forces are poorly equipped with antitank weapons and devices, the fact is stated in the *logistics* part of the subparagraph and the extent to which this is an exploitable vulnerability is briefly discussed. The intelligence officer might state, *"The guerrilla forces in our area are poorly equipped with antitank weapons and devices. They cannot effectively defend against armored vehicles."* The inability to defend against armored vehicles is carried forward to the *conclusions* paragraph as vulnerability.

To properly judge enemy peculiarities and weaknesses, the intelligence officer must have a well-rounded background in all phases of military operations and an excellent knowledge of enemy doctrine and past practices. Typical peculiarities and weaknesses involving personnel include shortages and overages in specialists, exceptionally high or low morale, and high rates of sickness. Peculiarities and weaknesses in the field of intelligence include susceptibility to deception or neutralization of certain enemy information collecting agencies, overdependence on certain sources of information, and ineffectiveness in certain types of intelligence operations. Operational peculiarities and weaknesses might include habitual repetition of certain maneuver schemes and unusual patterns of operations, faulty organization of the ground and disposition of reserves, susceptibility to electronic countermeasures, lack of adequate mobility, and inadequate air or artillery support and means of firing nuclear weapons. Logistic peculiarities and weaknesses might include shortages of certain essential supplies and material (including nuclear weapons), large concentrations of supplies, vulnerable points and bottlenecks in the logistic system, and inability to resupply during action. Civil affairs peculiarities and weaknesses might include hostile attitude of the civilian populace toward the enemy and inadequate control over movements of civilians.

ENEMY CAPABILITIES

In preparing the enemy capabilities paragraph of the intelligence estimate, a clear understanding of the nature of an enemy capability is necessary. Enemy capabilities are courses of action which the enemy can adopt and which will influence the accomplishment of the friendly mission, either favorably or unfavorably. A properly stated enemy capability indicates *what* the enemy can do, *when* he can do it, *where* he can do it, and *in what* strength he can do it. For example, *"Attack* (WHAT) *now* (WHEN) *along our front* (WHERE) *with 5 motorized rifle battalions supported by all available nuclear weapons, artillery and air* (STRENGTH)."

Another example, *"Conduct harassing operations* (WHAT) *at any time* (WHEN) *in our area* (WHERE) *with about 200 guerrillas armed with only small arms* (STRENGTH)."

The best plans and actions are based upon estimates of enemy *capabilities* and the probability of their adoption—and NOT upon enemy intentions. Enemy capabilities can be estimated objectively because they are based upon knowledge of the area of operations, enemy situation, enemy doctrine, and time and space factors. Intentions can seldom be determined. The enemy commander may change his mind or his higher commanders may change his orders. During World War I, the commander of the German Second Army, opposing the French Fifth Army at Guise, France, made 4 completely different decisions, and issued orders to carry them out, between 1730 hours 27 August 1914 and 0900 hours 28 August. In 1940, the British captured a German courier who had been forced down in the Netherlands and who carried plans for the German invasion of France through Belgium and Holland. The British and French, certain that the invasion would come through the historic route across the northern plains, concentrated their armies to the north—and were cut off from France. Hitler, knowing that this plan had been captured, had *changed* his plans and invaded across the Meuse River and through France.

Cover and deception operations may be practiced to indicate false intentions. After the battle of Tunisia, during World War II, the Allies decided to invade Italy via Sicily. To mislead the Germans, the British put false plans on the body of a fictitious Royal Marine courier and dropped the body into the water where it would be washed ashore in Spain. The Germans were tricked by this apparently valid plan into spreading their defenses across Europe, even to the extent of moving warships away from the Sicily area. The ruse made the invasion of Sicily easier.

In considering enemy capabilities, actions which are grossly unreasonable or disadvantageous to the enemy are not included. For example, the enemy may be physically capable of disengaging troops *committed* in a distant area in order to employ them against the friendly force. However, in most circumstances the G2 does not consider this to be a capability because it is unreasonable.

Appendix XVII discusses in detail the development of enemy capabilities.

In the *analysis and discussion* of enemy capabilities, the evidence considered includes the characteristics of the area of operation and positive or negative enemy activities. A major obstacle across part of the friendly area is evidence that attack elsewhere is more likely. Low ceilings and low visibility are evidence that the enemy may not use all his available aircraft. Open, flat areas without any appreciable concealment are evidence that the enemy may not use guerrilla or infiltration forces. In analyzing and discussing each enemy capability, or appropriate combination, the intelligence officer judges from the *enemy* point of view the advantage or disadvantage in adopting the capability. In doing this, he considers the enemy doctrine and practices and the ultimate results of adoption or rejection of the particular capability. For example, *"The employment of the unidentified tank division at AULALA will deprive the enemy of the reserves to counterattack a penetration by either of the two friendly divisions to our south. Commitment of this tank division too early will result in the later defeat of the enemy."*

The selected *probable enemy courses of action* must be fully justified by the analysis and discussion of enemy capabilities. The selection must also be based on how the enemy probably views his own vulnerabilities as indicated by his doctrine and the personality of the enemy commander. Knowledge of past enemy actions under similar circumstances assists in making objective selections. Above all, guesses are avoided—the conclusions are based on the available evidence. In determining what the enemy is *most likely* to do, it is essential to avoid conclusions based on friendly doctrines and practices.

ENEMY VULNERABILITIES

Like enemy capabilities, the nature of a vulnerability must be fully understood or the conclusions of the intelligence estimate will not be meaningful and useful. An enemy vulnerability is any condition or circumstance of the enemy situation or the area of operations which makes the enemy especially liable to damage, deception, or defeat. The *conclusions* paragraph of the estimate considers only those enemy vulnerabilities which *may* be exploited by the command and higher and subordinate headquarters. The G3, however, is responsible for recommending which vulnerabilities should be exploited. Only actual vulnerabilities are listed. An exposed flank which the enemy cannot, with available forces, extend or refuse is a vulnerability. If, however, the enemy has reserves which can extend the flank, the open flank is a vulnerability only if those reserves are destroyed. This vulnerability could be stated as *"Enemy north flank open to envelopment subject to destruction of enemy reserves at ***."* In studying the enemy peculiarities and weaknesses to determine his vulnerabilities, the characteristics of the area, *all* aspects of the enemy situation, and the enemy's doctrine and practices must be considered.

Each exploitable vulnerability listed includes a brief statement of the effect of the vulnerability. The listing is not a repetition of a statement of peculiarity or weakness. For example, *"Limited capability to oppose armored vehicles"* is stated and not *"Shortage of antitank weapons."* The listing of enemy vulnerabilities does not mean that they can all be exploited at the same time. For example, the enemy may be vulnerable to both a penetration at night time and a daytime flank envelopment. The order of listing vulnerabilities does not matter.

APPENDIX XVII

DEVELOPMENT OF ENEMY CAPABILITIES

Usually, there are 4 possible general tactical operations. The enemy can attack, defend, withdraw, and can usually reinforce his committed units. These operations can usually be subdivided into many specific courses of action. For example, an attack may be a penetration, an envelopment, or a turning movement. A defense may be in one position or in successive positions, and may be either static or mobile.

WHAT CAN THE ENEMY DO?

The specific activities which the enemy can perform depend upon the available units and equipment and the conditions under which they can be used. Consequently, the *what* of each enemy capability is determined by studying the area, the friendly situation, and the enemy units and equipment. Such a study usually indicates that the enemy can do certain things, but that others are impracticable. For example, the enemy can envelop only when there is an assailable flank, and can conduct airborne operations only when he has the necessary troops and aircraft.

WHEN?

The *time* at which the enemy can put into effect any of his capabilities depends upon his dispositions. Committed forces can be employed without significant delay, and can attack or defend now. Units at some distance from the edge of the battle area cannot be committed immediately but must first move to the place of commitment. Complicated weapons such as long range missiles require time to set up after reaching launching sites. An enemy capability involving displacement of forces cannot be put into effect until sometime after the force has started to move. Reserves must first be moved to appropriate locations such as attack positions or forward assembly areas. Consequently, time and space factors must be calculated in determining the

206

when of a capability involving the displacement of forces or equipment. These calculations are discussed later in this appendix.

The *when* is usually omitted from a statement of the enemy air, nuclear, chemical, and biological capabilities and other capabilities if *at any time* is intended. References to *when* are also omitted from statements of enemy capabilities to withdraw and the delay in successive positions because such actions can be started at any time. In withdrawal capabilities, the time of the start or completion of the withdrawal may be stated. For example, *"The enemy cannot withdraw beyond our objective until at least three hours after starting movement."*

WHERE?

The *where* of an enemy capability depends upon the weather, terrain, and disposition of his forces. Under existing and predictable conditions of weather, the terrain may provide avenues of approach into the friendly position from certain directions. It may also prevent the enemy's use of armored, mechanized, or airborne forces in certain areas. Cross compartments may provide the enemy with defense or delaying positions. The existence of suitable objectives and drop or landing zones, indicates where airborne forces may be employed. The presence of suitable beaches suggests where enemy amphibious forces may land. Accordingly, the *where* of each enemy capability is determined by analysis and integration of the characteristics of the area and the situations of the opposing forces. If the enemy is capable of launching an attack, the G2 asks himself in effect, *"Where can he do it?"* If the enemy defends, he asks, *"Where are suitable defensive positions and to what places must reinforcements be moved before they can be committed?"* If the enemy delays in successive positions he asks, *"Where are the favorable delaying positions?"* If the enemy can attack and the situation and the area indicate that the attack may be made anywhere along the front, the enemy capability may be stated in part as, *"Attack along our front ***."* In other circumstances, enemy capabilities may be stated in part as *"Attack to envelop* OUR NORTH FLANK ***.*"*, or *"Attack in the* DIRECTION BEIRUT-ACRE,*"* or *"Land (amphibious or airborne) forces in the* VICINITY OF TRENTAKURVA.*"* Partial statements of an enemy defense capability may include: *"Defend in his present position . . ."* or, *"Defend the line of the* OB RIVER ***." Delay capabilities may state, *"Delay in his* PRESENT *and successive positions to the* LINE OF THE HAN RIVER ***," or *"Delay along the general lines* PAULUS-JOANA, ELLI-ETTIKA, ***." Partial statements of the enemy's reinforcement capability may be, *"Reinforce an envelopment of our north flank* ***" or *"Reinforce his defense of the line ZIVA-CHEECH."*

IN WHAT STRENGTH?

The strength the enemy can use in a capability depends upon the composition, dispositions, and strength of his available forces. Forces which the enemy has committed against the friendly force can be used in almost any capability the enemy chooses to adopt. If 6 rifle battalions are committed against a division, the enemy can attack, defend or delay with the 6 rifle battalions supported by all available artillery, air, and nuclear weapons, etc.

In addition to the forces committed, the enemy can also use his available reserves. If the enemy has 6 battalions committed and 1 regiment in reserve, he can usually reinforce either his attack or his defense with the reserve regiment. This capability can be stated in part as, *"Attack now to envelop our north flank* WITH 6 RIFLE BATTALIONS SUPPORTED BY ALL AVAILABLE ARTILLERY, AND NUCLEAR WEAPONS, AIR, REINFORCED BY 1 RIFLE REGIMENT *at the following times and places* ***."

The statement of strength usually includes only close combat units such as infantry, armored, guerrilla, and reconnaissance units and their combat support such as artillery, air, nuclear weapons, and chemical units. The *number* and *details* of available supporting artillery, air, and similar units are specified in the *strength* subparagraph of the intelligence estimate and are usually not repeated in the statement of a capability involving support of close combat units. The numbers and types of sorties or weapons such units can deliver are usually stated in detail in a separate capability statement. *In what strength* is omitted in stating enemy capabilities to withdraw and delay because it is implied that all available forces will be involved.

SUPPORT OF CLOSE COMBAT FORCES

Some enemy capabilities refer specifically to the support of close combat forces rather than to the capabilities of close combat units. Such capabilities include: air; nuclear, chemical, and biological warfare; cover and deception; and electronic warfare capabilities. Some of these support capabilities, such as use of electronic warfare and cover and deception, are stated only when they significantly affect the accomplishment of the friendly mission. Statements of such capabilities include *when* and *where* the capability can be effective, and the enemy resources available or the results that can be accomplished. The *where* is omitted if anywhere throughout the unit area of operations is meant. For example, *"Start cover and deception operations at any time to include imitative and manipulative transmissions and use of special units capable of depicting two divisions, either tank or motorized rifle,"* or *"The enemy can intercept and jam our electromagnetic radiations at any time from any areas where he has line of sight to our transmitters and to the receivers to be jammed."*

TIME FACTOR IN COMMITTING TROOPS

The time required for the enemy to move troops and then commit them is determined on the basis of factors derived from analysis of past similar enemy movements. To determine the time when the enemy can commit a reinforcement unit, it is necessary to calculate the travel time from the unit location to a logical point where the unit can be committed. To the travel time is added the time required for assembling (closing time) enough of the unit to be used in coordinated action. Travel time plus closing time is the time after starting movement when the reinforcement can be considered completed. Except when an enemy unit is under continuous observation, it is assumed that any unit can start to move immediately after the time it is located. The earliest time the enemy can reinforce is the sum of the travel time, the closing time and the time last seen. For example, if an enemy reinforcement was last seen at 0800 hours and it can be used to envelop our north flank 1 hour after starting movement, it is assumed that the attack can be launched as early as 0900 hours (0800 plus 1 hour). In the exceptional case involving piecemeal commitment of enemy reinforcements, travel time only is considered. Forces which are committed piecemeal do not close into an assembly area or attack position before commitment.

Because observation of reinforcements is rarely continuous, statements of enemy reinforcing capabilities should include both the earliest time and the time after starting movement when the reinforcement can be made. For example, *"The enemy can reinforce his attack with the 45th Rifle Regiment at 0900 hours, or 1 hour after starting movement."* When the time since the last report is greater than the *after starting movement* time, only the *after starting movement* time is given. For example, *"The enemy can reinforce his attack with the 45th Rifle Regiment now, or 1 hour after starting movement."* When the number of reinforcements is large, or the enemy is capable of reinforcing in several areas, reinforcing capabilities are presented in tabular form. For example, *"The enemy can reinforce his attack or his defense with all or part of the following units at the places and times indicated below:*

Unit	Place	Motor	Foot
45th Rifle Regt	RJ 638	Now or 1 hr after starting movement	091200 Jun or 4 hr after starting movement
	RJ 888	090930 Jun or 1 hr 30 min after starting movement	091600 Jun or 8 hr after starting movement
37th Rifle Regt	RJ 638	091000 Jun or 2 hr after starting movement	100730 Jun or 23 hr 30 min after starting movement
	RJ 888	090930 Jun or 1 hr 30 min after starting movement	091430 Jun or 6 hr 30 min after starting movement

In selecting a logical point for reinforcement, area characteristics as avenues of approach, and logical enemy reactions to friendly courses of action are considered. For reinforcement of an attack capability, attack positions are selected for battalions and regiments, and forward assembly areas for division and larger units. For units moving to reinforce a defense, counterattack or defense positions are selected. For movements by aircraft, logical landing or drop zones from which the enemy forces can materially affect the accomplishment of the mission are selected.

The time required by the enemy to entruck, detruck, issue extra ammunition, make detailed reconnaissance, issue orders, deploy, or move from an attack position to a line of departure, is not considered because all may be completed before starting the operation or simultaneously with the movement. Until experience factors against a particular enemy are developed, the guidance below will assist in calculating reinforcement times.

Calculate foot marching time for all appropriate reinforcements unless the unit is observed in vehicles. Calculate motor movement time only for distances greater than 5 miles.

Consider foot marches of more than 20 miles and wheeled vehicle movements of more than 175 miles as forced marches. Movements of more than 140 miles by units using mostly tracked laying vehicles should also be considered as a forced march.

At the beginning of morning nautical twilight *(BMNT)* and at the end of evening nautical twilight *(EENT),* if the column is not closing, change the rate of march from day to night or vice versa as appropriate. If the column is closing at either of these two times, do not change the rate of march.

To move an enemy battalion, move and close the entire unit. To move a unit of regimental or larger size, move and close 2/3 of the combat elements—that is 2 battalions of a regiment or 2 regiments of a division. To move a unit with a flexible organization, such as a US type armored division, move and close 2/3 of the entire unit.

APPENDIX XVIII

ESSENTIAL ELEMENTS OF INFORMATION AND OTHER INTELLIGENCE REQUIREMENTS

WHAT ARE EEI?

Essential elements of information *(EEI)* and other intelligence requirements are stated as short and simple questions. Usually they are about:

Enemy capabilities, including when, where, and strength;

Enemy vulnerabilities, including nature, extent, and permanence;

Enemy order of battle factors;

Terrain, including natural and artificial obstacles;

Weather.

The statement includes enough guidance for further development into orders and requests for specific information. This is accomplished by including questions on time, strength, area, and by directing special attention to specific units, areas, and activities. An item of information or intelligence which the unit standing operating procedure *(SOP)* orders collected and reported as a routine matter may become an *EEI*. For example, an SOP may require all units to report immediately *"known or suspected nuclear targets or indications of their existence or development."* Whether or not such items are in the unit SOP, they become *EEI if they are needed by the commander at a particular time in making a decision with an acceptable degree of confidence.*

PURPOSE OF EEI

EEI are announced to subordinate, higher, and adjacent commands to guide them in preparing collection plans and evaluating (pertinence) information by making known the commander's highest priority intelligence needs which they are capable of satisfying.

Announcement of *EEI does not ensure* the collection of the necessary information. Collection agencies normally cannot act only on the *EEI* without further orders and cannot furnish the

212

final and complete answers to them. Collection agencies furnish the information necessary to answer *EEI* and other intelligence requirements only in response to orders or requests for specific information. For example, an *EEI* might be, *"Will the enemy reinforce his units now in contact? If so, when, where, and in what strength?"* The answer to this question comes from the processing of information on the strength and movement of enemy reserves, locations of assembly areas, etc., which has been collected by many agencies as a result of orders and requests for specific information.

ACTION BY RECEIVING HEADQUARTERS

The *EEI* announced by each headquarters are analyzed by each receiving headquarters to determine if it can obtain information to answer the *EEI* and whether the collection of that information interferes with accomplishing its mission. If it seriously interferes (or the information cannot be obtained), the receiving headquarters does not repeat the *EEI* to its subordinate units. *EEI*'s are modified by lower units as required. For example, a corps *EEI* may ask, *"Where are possible crossings of the AVIA River in the corps zone? Special attention between LUBAVILLE and BATZI CITY."* Subordinate divisions modify the *EEI* to relate it to the division zone and direct attention only to the specific parts of the river line within the division boundaries.

ANNOUNCEMENT OF EEI

EEI are usually announced through fragmentary orders. They may be announced orally by the commander. They are also listed in paragraph 2 of the intelligence annex to an operation order and may be included in the coordination instructions of paragraph 3 of the operation order. Other intelligence requirements are *not* disseminated as such. Only the orders and requests for specific information to answer other intelligence requirements are sent to collection agencies.

EEI and other intelligence requirements are canceled or modified by fragmentary orders or by publishing in an operation order a new list of *EEI* and other intelligence requirements. *EEI* and other intelligence requirements on the enemy's adoption of a course of action before a specified time are automatically canceled when that time arrives. For example, an *EEI* or other intelligence requirement, which asks, *"Will the enemy attack before our attack?"* is automatically canceled when the friendly attack is launched.

USE OF EEI TO DETERMINE ENEMY CAPABILITIES

Enemy capabilities are usually the first consideration in determining *EEI* and other intelligence requirements because of the commander's concern with intelligence which confirms, changes, or refutes the existing intelligence estimate. Each enemy capability listed in the current intelligence estimate is usually the subject of *either* an *EEI* or another intelligence requirement. If knowledge of the implementation of a particular enemy capability is not available *when* needed by the commander in order to make a decision with reasonable confidence, then that enemy capability is an *EEI* rather than another intelligence requirement. All enemy capabilities are *not* necessarily the subjects of *EEI* or other intelligence requirements. Enemy capabilities for which there are no apparent possibilities of implementation, are not considered for *EEI* or other intelligence requirements. For example, when a delaying action is being conducted against advancing superior enemy forces, *EEI* and other intelligence requirements on enemy defense, delay, and withdrawal are not stated.

EEI and other intelligence requirements on enemy capabilities are not answered completely until the enemy has committed himself to a course of action. *Partial* answers are produced continually and result in progressive changes to the intelligence estimate. For example, efforts to determine in *what strength* the enemy may reinforce committed forces often produce changes in the estimate of enemy reinforcements, and of the enemy's capability to reinforce. Similarly, evidence that the enemy *has* reinforced certain units changes the estimate of the number of committed forces.

REQUIREMENTS FOR SPECIFIC INFORMATION

EEI or other intelligence requirements on enemy attack capabilities direct specific attention to definite areas and usually to specified times. These areas are usually avenues of approach deter-

mined by analysis of the area of operations and enemy dispositions. If the enemy can attack using several avenues of approach,
only one *EEI* or other intelligence requirement is stated with the
different avenues of approach indicated as areas to which special
attention is directed. Time of the enemy implementation of a
capability is most frequently stated when the friendly mission is
to attack. The time may be stated precisely or as *before our
attack*, depending on whether the time of the friendly attack has
been determined. Examples of properly stated *EEI* or other intelligence requirements are, *"Will the enemy attack before 170500
June? If so, when, where, and in what strength? Special attention to the axis OLEE-MONTAL." "Will the enemy attack? If so,
when, where, in what strength? Special attention the axis
TOKKOLI-YANGU and SUBANGERI-ALETHEA."*

ENEMY DEFENSE. Statements of *EEI* and other intelligence
requirements about enemy defense specifically state the line or
area concerned. For example: *"Will the enemy continue to defend
IN HIS PRESENT POSITION? If so, how will he organize the ground
and with what troops? Special attention to locations and activities
of reserves."* Or, *"Will the enemy defend THE LINE (AREA)
GARRO-ZIERA? If so, when, with what troops, and with what
organization of the ground? Special attention to forces now at
BASEHOR."*

ENEMY WITHDRAWAL. Statements on enemy withdrawal
unsually indicate the line or area beyond which the enemy's withdrawal is of particular interest, and may direct attention to a line
or area to which the enemy might withdraw. For example, *"Will
the enemy withdraw BEYOND OUR OBJECTIVE prior to or during
our attack? If so, to what positions? SPECIAL ATTENTION TO THE
LINE (AREA) AUS-MICHEN."*

ENEMY DELAYING ACTION. Statements concerning enemy
delaying actions also specify the lines or areas along which delaying positions may be organized. For example: *"Will the enemy
delay in his PRESENT and in SUCCESSIVE POSITIONS TO THE
ARBIS RIVER? Special attention to the LINES (AREAS) KEIM-
DUNNO AND DUGAS-MRAZEK."*

ENEMY REINFORCEMENT. Statements on reinforcement
ordinarily do not ask whether it is a reinforcement of an attack

or a defense. They simply ask whether available reserves may be used and when and where. Other *EEI* and other intelligence requirements ask specifically whether the enemy will attack or defend. Statements on reinforcement direct attention to known reserves. For example: *"Will the enemy reinforce units now in contact? If so, when, where and with what forces? Special attention to the* 45TH RIFLE REGIMENT AT AVA *and the* UNIDENTIFIED TANK DIVISION AT HEADLEYI."

ENEMY TACTICAL NUCLEAR CAPABILITY. When the enemy has a tactical nuclear capability, the statement of the *EEI* or other intelligence requirement may be, *"Will the enemy employ nuclear weapons against us? If so, when, where, how many, of what yield, and by what delivery means? Special attention to very heavy artillery units in the vicinity of SASFA and possible missile launchers in the vicinity of OSBORNOVITCH."*

OTHER ENEMY CAPABILITIES. Statements on other enemy capabilities might be, *"Will the enemy* USE GUERRILLA FORCES *in conjunction with his attack? If so, when, where and in what strength? Special attention to the heavily wooded area of NE-BESH." "Will the enemy* INFILTRATE *our lines? If so, when, where, and in what strength? Special attention to the swampy area east of OHNHAYS." "Will the enemy* USE AIRBORNE *forces in our sector? If so, when, where, and in what strength? What will be the direction and altitude of approach? What drop or landing zones will be used? Special attention to the area south of NARDS-DORF." "Will the enemy* USE AMPHIBIOUS FORCES *on our south flank? If so, when, where, in what strength? How many landing vehicles of what type will be employed? Special attention to beaches at IRVINEU and WALTIEU." "Will the enemy* USE CHEMICAL OR BIOLOGICAL AGENTS *against us? If so, what agents, when, where and by what delivery means? Special attention to heavy mortar and artillery units."*

EEI and other intelligence requirements on enemy air capabilities are rarely listed at division and corps. Intelligence on these capabilities is disseminated by the field army. When enemy air activity may be a controlling factor, a corps or division commander may appropriately designate an air *EEI*, especially during the planning phases of an operation. However, it is not sent to *subordinate* units but only to higher headquarters.

ENEMY VULNERABILITY. *EEI* and other intelligence requirements may be announced in order to develop knowledge of enemy vulnerability to attack by nuclear weapons, and of other conditions which make the enemy liable to damage, deception, or defeat. *EEI* and other intelligence requirements of this type are used to produce intelligence on the nature, extent, permanence, or other details of the conditions which produce the vulnerability. *EEI* and other intelligence requirements on specific enemy vulnerabilities need not be stated if the answers to other *EEI* and intelligence requirements also develop the required intelligence on the specific vulnerability.

The details desired may be listed in the statement of *EEI* or other intelligence requirements or may be omitted if they are numerous and routine. For example, for analysis of nuclear targets, information is desired as to size, shape, composition, concentration, vulnerability, recuperability, and permanence. Since these details are both numerous and normal requirements, they are probably omitted from the statement. The statement may simply ask what nuclear targets exist in our zone and direct attention to specific area or activities.

When enemy vulnerabilities result from faulty dispositions, logistical inadequacies, or administrative deficiencies, the degree of permanence of the condition may have to be established before tactical plans to exploit the vulnerability can be prepared. Therefore, *EEI* or other intelligence requirements may ask "if" and "when" the condition may be corrected. For example, *"Will the enemy strengthen his north flank? If so, when, how, and with what troops or * * *."* or *"Will recent enemy personnel losses be replaced? If so, when and to what extent?"*

ENEMY ORDER OF BATTLE. *EEI* and other intelligence requirements on order of battle factors are often appropriate in long range planning, or when the enemy situation is very vague. Specific information on enemy dispositions, strength, or other order of battle factors may be lacking. For example, in the early planning phase of an amphibious operation, an *EEI* might be, *"What enemy forces will oppose our landing? What will be their* *composition, strength, and dispositions?"* Similarly, when the enemy situation is vague, an *EEI* or other intelligence requirement might state, *"What are the identification, composition, strength, and dispositions of forces to our front?"* and *"What forces are available to reinforce units now in contact?"*

TERRAIN CONDITIONS. *EEI* and other intelligence requirements on terrain conditions are frequently required in *offensive* operations. Information is usually sought about obstacles which may influence either friendly or enemy courses of action. An appropriate statement might be, *"What natural or artificial obstacles or barriers exist within the division zone? What are their nature and extent? Special attention to the PASKUNOK and AKCHEN areas."* Other terrain items, such as cross-country trafficability and the condition of road and rail lines, may also be the subjects of *EEI,* and other intelligence requirements. In the defense, *EEI* and other intelligence requirements on terrain under enemy control may be required in order to better determine enemy capabilities and vulnerabilities.

APPENDIX XIX

PREPARATION OF THE COLLECTION WORKSHEET

An example of a partially completed collection worksheet is given in figure 41.

SPECIFIC ORDER OR REQUEST

There are frequent duplications in the column for specific orders and requests. Not every entry is the basis for a *separate* order or request. The same item of specific information may be sought in connection with several different indications. For example, indications of attack may include, *"Location of artillery well forward";* indications of defense may include, *"Location of artillery laterally and in depth."* In both cases, the specific information desired is locations of artillery, by type and caliber.

LISTING OF COLLECTION AGENCIES

All available collection agencies are usually listed at the top of column 4 of the collection worksheet. Military intelligence specialist agencies such as prisoner of war interrogators and photo-interpreters may be specifically listed or grouped together. Supporting intelligence collection agencies are also listed. Opposite each basis for specific orders or requests, a cross, *X,* is entered in the column of each collection agency which is *capable* of furnishing the required information. Applying the factors of suitability, multiplicity, and balance, circles are drawn around the *X* of the agencies to be ordered or requested to furnish the information except for SOP items for agencies under the control of the headquarters.

TIME INFORMATION IS TO BE REPORTED

In considering the time of reporting information, consideration is given to the fact that information may be required by a certain time, at a specified time or times, at specified intervals, or upon the occurrence of specific events. A one-time report, such as the condition of a river bottom, may be required by a specified time.

Reports on certain enemy activities may be desired at specified times. For example, such a report may be required daily, at the beginning of morning nautical twilight *(BMNT)* and at the end of evening nautical twilight *(EENT)*. Reports of other enemy activities, such as movement along particular roads, may be required periodically. For example, *"Every 4 hours beginning at 0800."* Reports of identification of new units, enemy aerial activity, artillery bombardment, nuclear activity, and similar items, are usually required *as obtained*. Periodic negative reports pertaining to specified activities may also be required. The time of reporting of information is determined in consultation with the operations officer. Information which arrives too late is of no value. Information received too soon may be inaccurate by the time it is used. When obtaining the required information requires preparation by the collection agency, allowance is made for the time required for issuance of orders, preparation of personnel for the mission, execution of the mission, and the reporting of the results.

USE OF NOTES

Miscellaneous notes on the progress of the collection effort and notes for future action are recorded in column 6, *Remarks*. A code consisting of plus and minus signs, check marks, and crosses should be used for showing whether positive or negative reports have been received, whether information is inadequate, or whether the indication concerned has been substantiated. Notes on future cancellation or implementation of orders and requests, modifications of *EEI* and other intelligence requirements upon the occurrence of specific events, or other action to be taken as the collection effort progresses, should also be entered in column 6.

RELATION TO UNIT SOP

Because the collection worksheet helps ensure complete analysis of the *EEI* and other intelligence requirements and that necessary orders and requests have been sent out, entries *are also* made on information items which the unit SOP directs reporting. For example, SOP's ordinarily direct subordinate units to report new identifications as obtained. Nevertheless, the collection worksheet is completed with respect to new unit identifications exactly as it would be if the SOP did not require such reporting. However, for such items the X under agencies to be used need not be encircled and *SOP* may be entered in the *Remarks* column to indicate that an order is not necessary. If the basis for specific orders or requests directs attention to a specific area, the item is treated as if it were not an SOP item even though it may be information of the type covered in the unit SOP. For example, the unit SOP may prescribe reporting the location of hostile minefields, demolitions, and other defensive works. However, a requirement for reporting the locations of minefields in the vicinity of a specific area is *not* treated as an SOP item.

ORDERS AND REQUESTS

The wording of an order or request is not necessarily the same as the entry in the collection work-sheet on which it was based. Frequently the contents of several entries are combined into a single fragmentary order. Orders and requests for specific information are sent out either as fragmentary orders or by means of the intelligence annex to the operation order or plan (see appendix XX). Fragmentary orders are most frequently used because information requirements continually change. These orders and requests must be given the appropriate security classification because knowledge of the friendly requirements gives the enemy a basis for deducing the extent of the friendly knowledge of his situation and the friendly possible intentions.

Paragraph 3 of the intelligence annex, *Orders and Requests for Information,* implements the collection worksheet and contains a complete list of orders and requests for information that are in effect. Except for collection orders which are a part of the unit SOP, previously issued collection orders and requests *not* repeated in the intelligence annex are automatically cancelled.

EXAMPLE OF A PARTIALLY COMPLE

UNIT: 20th Inf Div
Period covered: From: 131530 Jul. To: Capture of high ground at 1055–1457.

(1) Commander's intelligence priorities and other required intelligence items	(2) Indications (analysis of items in column 1)	(3) Basis for specific orders or requests and notes for future action	1st BG, 61st Inf	2d BG, 62d Inf
EEI 1. What are the enemy dispositions? Special attention to organization of the ground, troops occupying strong points, and locations and activities of reserves.	a. Location and strengths of— (1) Units in contact. (2) Reserves. (3) Artillery. (4) Others.	(1) Report location, strength, and activities of troops on JANINA–CELINA Ridge.		⊗
		(2) Report location and strength of occupied strong points vicinity Hill 408 (1651) and Hill 282 (1251).		⊗
		(3) Report location and strength of occupied strong points vicinity PLATEAU BELLERIVE.	⊗	
		(4) Report location and strength of occupied strong points vicinity BRAZOS Woods.	⊗	⊗
		(5) Report location and strength of occupied strong points on PETROV Woods Ridge vicinity 2050.	⊗	
		(6) Report location and strength of occupied strong points on PETROV Woods Ridge vicinity 1849.		⊗
		(7) Report location and strength of troops in LARUNA River Valley vicinity LEON (1647).		
		(8) Report location and strength of troops vicinity Hill 326 (1153).		⊗
		(9) Report location of all artillery and mortar positions in zone to include those unoccupied and number of pieces.	⊗	⊗
	b. Presence of demolitions, gassed areas, radiological and biological contamination, obstacles, and minefields.	(10) Report location and extent of demolitions, gassed areas, radiological and biological contamination, obstacles, and minefields to front, flanks, and forward of present position.	X	X
	c. Entrenching and erecting bands of wire.	(11) Report hostile entrenching and erection of bands of wire along present line of contact.	⊗	⊗
		(12) Report hostile entrenching and bands of wire on JANINA–CELINA Ridge.		⊗
	d. Dumping ammunition and engineer supplies and equipment, fortifying buildings.	(13) Report evidences of fortification of buildings in zone, particularly WACO (1451) and ST GEORGE (1554).		⊗
	e. Location of command posts and supply and evacuation installations.	(14) Report location of command posts and supply and evacuation installations in division zone north of road LA PALOMA–WACO special attention to vicinity CR 1356.		
Other Intelligence requirements 2. Will the enemy attack prior to 140430 July? If so, when, where, and in what strength? Special attention to the axes LEON (1647)–OSTRO (2046); Hill 406 (1849)–Hill 418 (1848).	a. Movement of hostile units forward.	(15) Report volume and type of traffic across TAKASAN Canal and on roads leading south from CELINA, JANINA, CR 1356, and CR 1255.		
	b. Location of enemy troops in forward assembly areas.	(16) Report location of troops, types, and numbers, vicinity 1550.		
		(17) Report location of troops, types, and numbers vicinity 1851.		⊗
	c. Clearing of lanes through obstacles within own position.	(18) Report clearing of lanes through obstacles within Aggressor position in zone.	⊗	⊗
	d. Increased patrolling.	(19) Report the number, size, composition, routes, and time observed of enemy patrols in zone.	⊗	⊗
	e. Establishment and strengthening of counterreconnaissance screen.	(20) Report activity and size of units blocking our patrolling along line of contact.	⊗	⊗
	f. Extensive artillery preparations.	(21) Report any marked change in artillery fire to include time, location, direction of fire, number of rounds, rate and caliber received in zone or area.	X	X
	g. Increased air reconnaissance.	(22) Report amount and type of air activity in zone or area.	X	X
	h. Forces in contact being replaced or reinforced by new units.	(23) Report new identifications.	X	X

Figure 41. Example of a partially completed collection worksheet.

TED COLLECTION WORKSHEET

3d BG, 63d Inf	4th BG, 64th Inf	5th BG, 65th Inf	1st Cav Sq, 21st Cav	1st Med Tk Bn, 1st Armor	Div Arty	20th Engr Bn	20th Avn Co	Co B, ASA Div Spt Co	55th Inf Div	22d Inf Div	I Corps	Auxiliary agencies	Hour and destination of reports	Remarks
													(4) Agencies to be used	**(5)** / **(6)**
	⊗			⊗		⊗	⊗		X		⊗	⊗	(1) As obtained. Negative reports every 2 hours starting 131800 July.	Assign to 3/63 when committed. ✓
							⊗		X		X	⊗	(2) Same as (1).	✓
	⊗			⊗		X				X	⊗		(3) Same as (1).	+
	⊗			⊗		X				X	⊗		(4) Same as (1).	✓
	⊗			⊗		X					⊗		(5) Same as (1).	✓
	⊗			⊗		X					⊗		(6) Same as (1).	If positive, notify I Corps without delay and make maximum effort to get details for target analysis. +
	⊗			⊗	⊗						⊗		(7) Same as (1).	If positive, notify 22 Inf Div and I Corps. +
	⊗			⊗		X				X	⊗		(8) Same as (1).	Cancel after damage assessment reports received. ✓
	⊗			⊗		⊗	⊗		X	X	⊗	⊗	(9) As obtained.	Check corps and army PERINTREPs. ✓
			X		X	X			X	X	X	X	(10) As obtained.	SOP. +
	⊗			⊗							⊗		(11) As obtained.	Cancel at 140430. ✓
	⊗			⊗							⊗	⊗	(12) As obtained.	✓
										X	⊗		(13) As obtained.	If no information by 132300, try I Corps. ✓
	⊗			⊗		⊗	⊗				⊗	⊗	(14) As obtained.	+
	⊗			⊗		⊗	⊗		X	X	⊗	⊗	(15) Same as (1).	Assign to 1/61, 2/62 when railroad through LAY is reached. ✓
	⊗			⊗		X					⊗		(16) As obtained.	Cancel at 140430. ✓
				⊗		X					⊗		(17) As obtained.	Cancel at 140430. ✓
						X	⊗	X					(18) As obtained.	Cancel at 140430. +
⊗	⊗	⊗	⊗	⊗	⊗								(19) As obtained.	✓
				⊗									(20) As obtained.	Cancel at 140430. ✓
X	X	X	X	X	X	X	X						(21) As obtained.	SOP. +
X	X	X	X	X	X		X						(22) As obtained.	SOP. +
			X					⊗	X	X	X	X	(23) As obtained.	SOP. +

Figure 41 (Continued.)

APPENDIX XX

FORMAT AND EXAMPLE OF AN INTELLIGENCE ANNEX TO AN OPERATION ORDER

FORMAT

Copy Nr _____
Unit
Location
Date Time Group
Msg Reference Nr.

Annex _____ (Intel) to OPORD _____
Reference:

1. SUMMARY OF ENEMY SITUATION:
May refer to an ISUM, overlay, or other intelligence document.

2. EEI AND OTHER INTELLIGENCE REQUIREMENTS:
   a. EEI
      (List in sequence.)
   b. Other Intelligence Requirements.
      (List in sequence.)

3. ORDERS AND REQUESTS FOR INFORMATION:
   May be an appendix. Contains a complete list of all *current* collection orders and requests to higher, lower, and adjacent units. Previously issued orders and requests not part of the unit standing operating procedure are automatically canceled if not repeated.

4. MISCELLANEOUS:
   List under separate subparagraphs any items not covered in the previous paragraphs or which require action different from that prescribed in the unit standing operating procedure for handling of prisoners of war, deserters, defectors, repatriates, captured documents, captured material, issue of maps and photos, counterintelligence, reports and distribution, and auxiliary agencies. Subparagraphs not required are not listed and the remaining subparagraphs are relettered in sequence. In preparing this paragraph, supporting intelligence agencies are consulted as appropriate.
   a. Instructions for handling prisoners of war, enemy deserters, liberated civilians, evaders, escapers, refugees, displaced persons, and repatriates to insure their maximum exploitation as sources of information. This subparagraph may include instructions for initial interrogation, search, segregation, special handling of personnel of particular categories (e.g., high ranking officers), special handling of suspect civilians, or special lines of inquiry to

224

be pursued in interrogating personnel. Appropriate references are made to the "Counterintelligence" subparagraph.

b. Instructions for handling and processing captured documents. May also include instructions on the search for and processing of documents of a particular type, special handling of documents found on prisoners of war, and may specify documents for which special search is to be made.

c. Specify enemy material particularly desired for examination and include any special instructions for processing enemy material.

d. Maps and photos to be supplied for the operation including each classification or scale to be furnished each unit, and instructions on special requisitions and distribution.

e. Instructions on safeguarding of military information; radio and radar silence; communications security monitoring, censorship, compromise of signs, countersigns, paroles, codes or other classified matters; camouflage, dispersion, and light discipline; handling of apprehended friendly deserters, and enemy and friendly civilians; and similar matters. If the information and instructions are voluminous, use a counterintelligence appendix.

f. Nonroutine instructions on the submission of intelligence reports and distribution of intelligence publications.

g. Use of specialized intelligence agencies to include:

(1) Agencies which are controlled by the intelligence officer.

(2) Agencies of higher headquarters with elements under the operational control of the intelligence officer.

(3) Agencies supervised by other staff sections but whose operations require close coordination with the intelligence officer.

This subparagraph rarely appears in the intelligence annex of a division operation order.

h. Items not properly included in the previous subparagraphs. May contain special instructions pertaining to radiological survey and monitoring, etc.

Acknowledge.

Commander

Appendixes: Material of interest to a few, or which is detailed or voluminous. When appendixes are used, refer to them in appropriate parts of the annex.

Distribution:

Authentication:

EXAMPLE

INTELLIGENCE ANNEX TO DIVISION OPERATION ORDER

> Copy Nr 5
> 20th Inf Div
> TARNAU (9306), GERMANY
> 060600 August 19_____
> XP 35

Annex A (Intel) to OPORD 4
Reference: Map, GERMANY-POLAND, 1:100,000, CZESTOCHOWA-
ZAWIERCIE

1. SUMMARY OF ENEMY SITUATION:
    a. Appendix 1, Situation Overlay and ISUM NR 55.
    b. Aggressor is apparently withdrawing to the WARTA River line to
    defend in that vicinity.

2. EEI AND OTHER INTELLIGENCE REQUIREMENTS:
    a. EEI:
    What are the enemy dispositions? Special attention to ***.
    b. Other Intelligence Requirements:
       (1) Will the enemy continue to withdraw to * * *?
       (2) Will the enemy delay or defend west of * * *? Special atten-
       tion to * * *.

                    * * * * * * *

3. ORDERS AND REQUESTS FOR INFORMATION:
    a. Appendix 2, Air Recon Plan.
    b. Orders to attached and subordinate units.
       (1) All Units: Report, as obtained; negative report every 4 hours
       beginning 061000 August.
          (a) Interception of any enemy patrols equipped for CB war-
          fare activity.

                 *   *   *   *   *   *

       (2) 1st BG, 61st Inf.
          (a) Report as obtained; negative report every 2 hours begin-
          ning 061000 August. Location and strength of occupied
          strong points in vicinity of * * *.

                 *   *   *   *   *   *

    c. Requests to higher, adjacent, and cooperating units.
       (1) 1st Corps is requested to provide information, as obtained, of —

                 *   *   *   *   *   *

          (c) Disposition of Aggressor rifle corps located vicinity of
          * * *.

          (d) Volume and type of traffic across * * *.

                 *   *   *   *   *   *

(2) 72d and 55th Inf Div are requested to provide information, as obtained, of —

         *   *   *   *   *   *

(c) Location of missile and rocket launcher sites.

(d) New identifications, particularly of CB units and their location.

         *   *   *   *   *   *

(3) Co A, 305th ASA Bn is requested to provide information, as obtained, of —

(a) Locations of enemy command posts, supply and evacuation installations. Special attention to vicinity of * * *.

(b) Movement of hostile units. Special attention to * * *.

         *   *   *   *   *   *

4. MISCELLANEOUS:

a. Prisoners of war from the 7th Arty Corps will be reported to division G2 without delay.

         *   *   *   *   *   *

c. Requests for preplanned airphoto missions due at division CP by 1400 daily, effective 6 August 19——.

d. Continuous monitoring starting 060830 and continuing until further notice from this headquarters.

Acknowledge.

SHORT
Maj Gen

Appendixes: 1—Situation
                   Overlay (omitted)
           2—Air Reconnaissance
                   Plan (omitted)

Distribution: A

OFFICIAL:

/s/Davidson

DAVIDSON
G2

APPENDIX XXI

COUNTERINTELLIGENCE ESTIMATE FORMAT

Issuing section and headquarters[1]
Place
Date and Time

COUNTERINTELLIGENCE ESTIMATE NR:
Reference: Maps or charts or other documents.

1. MISSION:
   State the assigned or assumed mission.
2. THE AREA OF OPERATIONS:
   This paragraph discusses characteristics of the area and their effect on enemy intelligence, subversive, and sabotage operations and on our counterintelligence operations and measures.
   a. Weather.
      (1) Existing situation.
      (2) Effect on enemy intelligence, subversive, and sabotage operations.
      (3) Effect on our counterintelligence operations and measures.
   b. Terrain.
      Analyze under the same headings as weather.
   c. Other characteristics. The following additional characteristics are considered, as pertinent, in separate subparagraphs: sociology politics, economics, psychology, and other factors. Other factors may include such items as science, material, transportation, manpower and hydrography. They are analyzed under the same headings as weather.

Note. [1] If distributed outside the headquarters, the first line of the heading is the official designation of the issuing command and the ending modified accordingly.

3. ENEMY INTELLIGENCE, SABOTAGE, AND SUBVERSIVE SITUATION:
   a. Disposition.
   b. Composition.
   c. Strength, including efficiency of enemy intelligence, subversive, and sabotage organization.
   d. Recent and present significant intelligence, subversive, and sabotage activities (including enemy's knowledge of our intelligence situaation).
   e. Peculiarities and weaknesses.

4. ENEMY INTELLIGENCE, SABOTAGE, AND SUBVERSIVE CAPABILITIES:
   a. List all capabilities under the following headings:
      (1) Intelligence. (Include all methods of which the enemy is known or estimated to be capable.)
      (2) Sabotage. (Include all capabilities of military, political, and economic sabotage possible of execution by agents and guerrillas.)
      (3) Subversion. (Include all types, such as psychological warfare propaganda, sedition, treason, disaffection, affecting own troops, allies, local civilians, and assistance in evasion and escape of hostile civilians.
   b. Analysis and discussion of enemy capabilities to provide a basis for conclusions as to relative probability of adoption of enemy intelligence, subversive, and sabotage capabilities.

5. CONCLUSIONS:
   a. Relative probability of adoption of enemy intelligence, subversive, and sabotage capabilities.
   b. Effects the capabilities will have on our courses of action including requirements for counterintelligence measures.

/s/ ....
Chief, Counterintelligence Branch

PARTIALLY COMPLETED COUNTERINTELLIGENCE MEASURES WORKSHEET

UNIT: 20th Inf Div
Period covered: From 180800 August TO: Seizure of SHMENDRICK and destruction of enemy in zone.

(1) Phases or periods of the operation	(2) Categories of counterintelligence activities involved	(3) Counterintelligence measures to be adopted	Civil affairs platoon	Signal officer	Public information officer	Provost marshal	ASA support company	All units	Aviation officer	Division artillery	Security section	(5) Instructions regarding entries in columns 3 and 4, notes for future action and staff coordination measures
Period in assembly areas before attack.	1. MILITARY SECURITY a. Secrecy discipline.	(1) Cover or paint all vehicle and aircraft markings.						⊗	⊗			Coordinate with G4. Provost marshal report violations.
		(2) Remove identifications from uniforms.						⊗				Coordinate with G1. Provost marshal report violations.
		(3) Restrict personnel to areas except when on official business.						⊗				Coordinate with G1. Provost marshal report violations.
		(4) Emphasize security discipline in command posts, and elsewhere, with particular reference to handling of documents and maps, phone conversations, loose talk, and speculation which might convey information to the enemy. All personnel will be instructed regarding same.						⊗			⊗	Coordinate with G3. Security section assist with instruction and check.
		(5) Report all breaches and suspected compromise of security at once to G2.										SOP
	b. Security of nuclear weapons and delivery systems.	(6) Disseminate location of nuclear weapons on need-to-know basis.					⊗	X		⊗	⊗	Coordinate with G1, G3, and G4.
		(7) Nuclear weapons units draw all supplies from division distributing points by use of own vehicles.								⊗		Coordinate with G4.
		(8) Collect and place under guard or evacuate, as determined appropriate by unit commander, civilians in position to observe nuclear weapons, storage, and delivery sites.								⊗		Coordinate with G5.
	c. Safeguarding of classified defense information and equipment.	(9) Check SOP plans for security of cryptographic devices; for destruction and for report of loss or compromise.		X			⊗				⊗	SOP. Security section check.
		(10) Check plans and equipment for destruction of		X				X				SOP. Security section check.

Figure 42A. Example of counterintelligence measures worksheet (partially completed).

								Remarks
d. Communication security.	(11) Maintain radio silence until further orders. No signal panels displayed. ...documents in event of imminent capture.			X				Coordinate with G3 and signal officer.
	(12) Check that unauthorized personnel are prohibited from entering message centers.			X				SOP.
	(13) Patrol all wire lines used by units of division.			X				SOP. Check with signal officer for compliance.
e. Security of troop movements.	(14) Cut all wire lines leading into Aggressor occupied territory.			X		⊗		Coordinate with I Corps and 22d Inf Div.
	(15) Prohibit movement of all military vehicles during hours of daylight except for staff parties and messengers authorized by battle group, separate battalion, trains commander, and higher headquarters.		⊗					Coordinate with G3 and G4. Provost marshal report violations.
	(16) Establish control posts to restrict unauthorized vehicle movements in and out of assembly areas. Prevent congregation of vehicles at command posts. Start control measures before establishment of command posts.			X				Coordinate with G1 and G4.
f. Security control of accredited correspondents.	(17) Escort all radio, press, and other civilian visitors to public information office at division command post.	⊗		⊗				Coordinate with public information officer.
	(18) Furnish accredited correspondents and photographers information subject to same restrictions as military personnel. Their credentials examined and approved by division G2 who will notify all concerned.	⊗		⊗				Coordinate with public information officer.
g. Concealment.	(19) Take oblique and vertical photos of bivouac area daily.			⊗	⊗			Coordinate with G3 and aviation officer.
	(20) Ensure that all stationary vehicles and installations are under natural concealment or camouflage.			X				SOP.
	(21) Black out all installations during darkness.			X				SOP. Provost marshal report violations.
	(22) Vehicles use blackout lights in night movement.			X				SOP.
	(23) Permit no open fires (except mess ranges) in assembly areas.			X				SOP.
	(24) Personnel and vehicles stop and remain motionless if a flare appears at night.			X				SOP.
	(25) Leave no paper, trash, or laundry exposed in assembly areas.			X				SOP. Security section inspect areas.

Figure 42B. Example of counterintelligence measures worksheet (partially completed) (cont.).

b. Counterespionage.	(26) Personnel and vehicles stop and remain motionless unless attacked if unidentified aircraft appears overhead during daylight.		⊗	SOP.
	(27) Division aircraft remain grounded and concealed except when cleared by division.		×	Coordinate with G3, G4, and aviation officer.
	(28) Conduct at least one inspection daily for violations of camouflage discipline.		⊗	Coordinate with G5, and G1.
	(29) Establish check points to prevent movement of unauthorized civilians into or out of troop areas. Violators taken to civilian enclosures at *** and ***.	⊗	⊗	SOP. Coordinate with G5 and G1.
	(30) All arrests of civilians violating security regulations made by military police or other overt personnel. Only those suspected of being enemy agents turned over to the security section.		⊗	Coordinate with G3.
c. Tactical measures.	(31) Place roadblocks around perimeter of bivouac.	×		Coordinate with G3, G4, and G1. Provost marshal report violations.
	(32) Limit all movement to zone of 22d Inf Div before attack to reconnaissance parties. Approval before each trip obtained from division headquarters.			SOP.
	(33) No firing at hostile planes unless directly attacked.	⊗	⊗⊗	Coordinate with G3.
	(34) Establish ground surveillance to detect enemy parachute drops, infiltrators, and guerrillas.	⊗	×	Coordinate with G3 and 1st Corps.
	(35) Guard bridge across the SCHLAMAZEL River.		⊗	Coordinate with G5.
	(36) Establish motor patrols and check points along highways to control and check movement of civilians.			Coordinate with G5. Notify all units and provost marshal.
2. CIVIL SECURITY a. Control of circulation.	(37) Restrict all civilians to area within 3 kilometers of homes. Permits to exceed this limit issued though civil affairs.	⊗	×	Provost marshal report violations. G5 disseminate to civilians.
b. Curfew.	(38) Forbid civilians to ride in military vehicles without authorization of unit commander.	×	⊗	Coordinate with G5.
c. Passes and permits.	(39) Enforce curfew for all civilians in area from 2000 to 0500 daily.	×	×	SOP.
d. Restricted areas.	(40) Enforce civilian pass system in accordance with theater pass plan.		×	Coordinate with G5.
	(41) Forbid civilians, other than those living in the area or employed by our forces, to enter troop areas.		×	

Figure 42C. Example of counterintelligence measures worksheet (partially completed) (cont.).

APPENDIX XXIII

INTELLIGENCE STAFFS

The intelligence staffs at division, field army, logistical command, and theater army headquarters are shown in figures 43, 44A, 44B, 45A, 45B, 46A, 46B, and 46C, below.

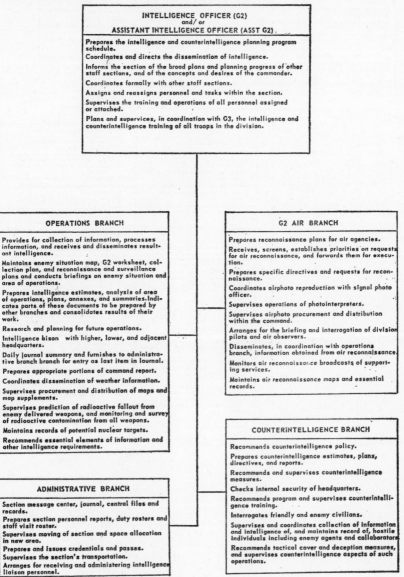

Figure 43. Intelligence section, division headquarters.

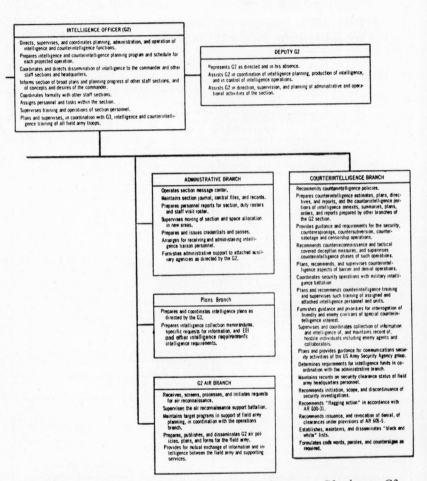

Figure 44A. Intelligence section, field army headquarters—G2, deputy G2, administrative branch, plans branch, G2 air branch, and counterintelligence branch.

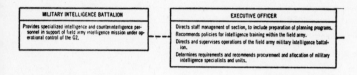

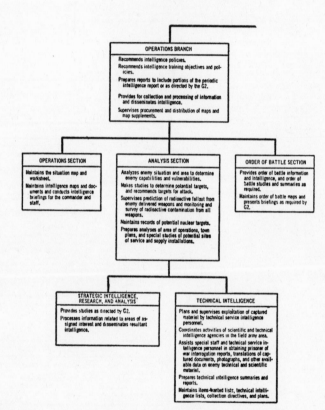

Figure 44B. Intelligence section, field army headquarters—executive officer, operations branch, and military intelligence battalion.

INTELLIGENCE OFFICER
and/or
EXECUTIVE

Prepares planning scheudules.
Directs and coordinates the dissemination of intelligence.
Coordinates formally with other staff divisions.
Assigns and reassigns personnel and tasks.
Requests procurement and directs the allocation and employment of military intelligence specialists and units.
Plans and supervises the training and operations of all intelligence personnel assigned or attached to the theater logistical command.
Plans and supervises the intelligence training of all troops assigned to the theater logistical command.

INTELLIGENCE BRANCH

Chief, intelligence branch.
Determines requirements for and recommends procurement and employment of military intelligence specialists and units.
Directs and supervises the preparation of appropriate parts of periodic intelligence reports and other pertinent documents.

Plans section.
Prepares and coordinates intelligence plans.

Operations section.
Provides for collection and processing of information, and disseminates resultant intelligence.
Maintains situation map and worksheet and conducts intelligence briefings for the commander and staff as required.
Prepares analyses of area of operations, town plans, and special studies of potential sites of service and supply installations.
Details attached interpreters as required.
Supervises procurement and distribution of maps and airphotos.
Supervises prediction of radioactive fallout from enemy delivered weapons and survey and monitoring of radioactive contamination from all weapons.

TECHNICAL INTELLIGENCE BRANCH

Plans for and supervises the exploitation of captured materiel.
Assists technical intelligence personnel.
Prepares technical intelligence summaries and reports.
Maintains inventory records and data on exploited materiel.
Prepares and publishes critical item lists.

Figure 45A. Intelligence division, directorate of security, theater army logistical command headquarters (type C logistical command)—intelligence officer and/or executive, intelligence branch, and technical intelligence branch.

ADMINISTRATIVE BRANCH

Chief, administrative branch.
Recommends intelligence administrative policy.

Prepares duty and staff visit roster for entire intelligence division.

Message center.
Maintains the division message center, journal, journal file, and routes incoming material for action or information.

Library and central files.
Maintains library of source and reference material, and central files for the intelligence division.
Establishes TOP SECRET control procedures for the intelligence division.

Personnel, supply, and fiscal section.
Determines requirements for, procures, distributes, and documents intelligence personnel, supplies, and funds.
Assigns office space and performs housekeeping tasks for the intelligence division.
Prepares all personnel reports for the intelligence division.

Publications section.
Reproduces, edits, and assembles all intelligence division publications and makes bulk distribution.

Liaison section.
Coordinates activities of intelligence liaison personnel.
Provides liaison officers to higher, lower, and adjacent headquarters.
Provides signal communications, transportation, etc., for liaison officers.
Receives, directs, and assists liaison officers from other headquarters.

COUNTERINTELLIGENCE BRANCH

Chief, counterintelligence branch.
Recommends counterintelligence policy.
Prepares counterintelligence estimates, plans, directives, and reports.
Recommends augmentation of security detachments.
Procures, distributes, and maintains records of counterintelligence funds, special equipment, and supplies.
Supervises and controls operations of security detachments.

Military security section.
Prepares estimates, plans, policies, directives, and reports for military security.
Recommends and supervises counterintelligence training.

Recommends policies and plans for assumption of counterintelligence control of army rear areas.
Prepares estimates, plans, directives for, and supervises for intelligence aspects of tactical cover and deception operations.

Civil security section.
Prepares estimates, plans, directives, policies for, and supervises all matters pertaining to civil security.
Interrogates friendly and enemy civilians.
Maintains records of enemy agents and collaborators.
Recommends policies and makes plans for assumption of civil security control of army rear areas.
Establishes liaison with military government, military police, indigenous authorities, and others, for counterintelligence activities within the theater logistical command area.

Port, frontier, and travel security section.
Prepares estimates, plans, directives, and policies on all matters pertaining to port, frontier, and travel security.
Supervises and coordinates port, frontier, and travel security policy.
Coordinates with Navy and Air Force on security of sea frontiers, seaports, and airports.

Special operations section.
Prepares estimates, plans, and directives for, and supervises and coordinates special counterintelligence operations.
Determines requirements for, procures, and employs special counterintelligence units, agents, and special counterintelligence funds, equipment, and supplies.
Establishes and operates special interrogation centers if required.
Plans for and supervises the execution of intelligence security throughout the theater logistical command area.

Censorship branch.
Recommends censorship policy, and procurement and employment of censorship units.
Prepares appropriate parts of periodic intelligence reports.
Prepares estimates, plans, directives, and policies on civil and military censorship in the theater army logistical command area.
Supervises and coordinates civil and military censorship activities.
Controls and supervises operations of censorship units attached to the theater army logistical command.
Maintains general and special watch lists.
Plans for and supervises censorship training of all theater army logistical command transient personnel and of unit and area censors.

Figure 45B. Intelligence division, directorate of security, theater army logistical command headquarters (type C logistical command)—administrative branch and counterintelligence branch.

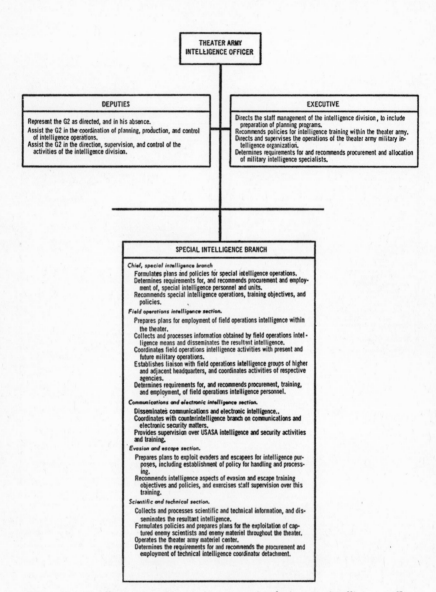

Figure 46A. Intelligence section, theater army headquarters—intelligence officer, deputies, executive, and special intelligence branch.

COMBAT INTELLIGENCE BRANCH	COUNTERINTELLIGENCE BRANCH
Chief, combat intelligence branch. Recommends intelligence policies. Recommends combat intelligence training objectives and policies.	**Chief, counterintelligence branch.** Recommends counterintelligence policy. Prepares counterintelligence estimates, plans, directives, and reports. Recommends augmentation of counterintelligence security detachments and units. Procures, distributes, and maintains records of counterintelligence funds, special equipment, and supplies. Supervises and controls operations of counterintelligence security unit.
Strategic and combat intelligence section. Prepares intelligence estimates, plans, annexes, summaries, and reports, Indicates parts of these to be prepared by other sections and branches, and coordinates the results of their work. Provides for the collection of strategic and combat information, processes the information received, and disseminates the resultant intelligence. Recommends policies governing responsibilities, functions, and procedures relative to combat intelligence within the theater army. Prepares and disseminates terrain, hydrographic, and weather studies and strategic studies of the theater army area. Recommends intelligence training objectives and policies, and supervises such training.	**Military security section.** Prepares estimates, plans, directives, and reports for all matters pertaining to military security and intelligence aspects of tactical cover and deception operations. Recommends military security policy. Supervises and coordinates military security activities. Determines requirements for and recommends employment of counterintelligence security units for military security purposes.
Order of battle section. Provides order of battle information and intelligence. Recommends theater army order of battle policies. Recommends order of battle training objectives and policies, and supervises such training.	**Civil security section.** Prepares estimates, plans, directives, and reports for all matters pertaining to civil security. Recommends civil security policy. Supervises and coordinates civil security activities. Determines requirements for, and recommends employment of, counterintelligence security units. Interrogates friendly and enemy civilians. Maintains records of enemy agents and collaborators. Establishes liaison with military government, indigenous authorities, and other agencies, for circulation control and other counterintelligence activities.
Interrogation section. Recommends policies, plans for, and supervises and coordinates the interrogation of prisoner of war and civilian refugees throughout the theater army. Controls interrogation agencies not assigned or attached to subordinate echelons. Operates the theater army interrogation center. Processes information obtained through interrogation and disseminates the resultant intelligence. Recommends interrogation training objectives and policies, and supervises such training.	**Port, frontier, and travel security section.** Prepares estimates, plans, directives, and reports for all matters pertaining to port, frontier, and travel security. Recommends port, frontier, and travel security policy. Supervises and coordinates port, frontier, and travel security operations. Coordinates with Navy and Air Force on security of sea frontiers, seaports, and airports. Determines requirements for and recommends employment of counterintelligence security units for port, frontier, and travel security.
Documents section. Recommends policies, plans, and supervises and coordinates the collection and exploitation of documents throughout the theater army. Controls document agencies not assigned or attached to subordinate echelons. Operates the theater army documents center. Processes information obtained through exploitation of documents and disseminates resultant intelligence. Recommends training objectives and policies for translator and documents personnel.	**Censorship section.** Recommends censorship policy. Prepares censorship estimates, plans, directives, and reports. Recommends procurement and employment of censorship units. Supervises and coordinates censorship activities. Maintains general and special watch lists. Plans for and supervises censorship training.
Target analysis section. Analyzes potential tactical and strategic targets, recommends attack on such targets, and makes assessments of damage inflicted. By study of enemy operations, industrial systems, lines of communications, and population centers, determines critical factors therein and their vulnerability to attack. Makes detailed examination of specific targets to ascertain their relative importance and vulnerability to attack with available weapons. Serves as secretariat and staff for a theater army target analysis and priority committee.	**Special operations section.** Prepares estimates, plans, directives, and reports for all matters pertaining to special counterintelligence operations. Supervises and coordinates special counterintelligence operations. Determines requirements for, procures, and employs special counterintelligence security units and agents, and issues special counterintelligence funds, equipment, and supplies. Establishes and operates special interrogation centers if required. Plans for and supervises the execution of intelligence security throughout the theater army.
War room section. Maintains the intelligence division war room. Provides administrative assistance for intelligence participation in the maintenance of other war rooms in the theater army headquarters. Provides briefing officers.	

Figure 46B. Intelligence section, theater army headquarters—combat intelligence branch and counterintelligence branch.

RECONNAISSANCE AND MAPPING BRANCH

Chief, reconnaissance and mapping branch.
Recommends map and airphoto policies.
Recommends training objectives and policies.

Operations section.
Recommends policies on visual and photo air reconnaissance and necessary plans and directives.
Determines requirements for, and recommends procurement and employment of, air-ground operations personnel.
Recommends training objectives and policies for air-ground operations personnel, and supervises such training.
Maintains information files on the location, characteristics, and significance of installations which may be targets.

Mapping and charting section.
Prepares plans and directives on procurement, production, and dissemination of maps and charts.
Supervises maintenance of theater army map library facilities.
Provides technical assistance to, and acts as secretariat for a theater army mapping committee.

Topographic and hydrographic section.
Prepares technical military and engineer studies of hostile installations.
Provides assistance in the preparation of analyses of area of operations and strategic studies of the theater army area.
Provides for production and distribution of terrain models required by theater army forces.

Airphoto section.
Determines future requirements for airphotos and prepares long-range photo reconnaissance plans.
Prepares plans, policies, and directives for the production and dissemination of photo intelligence and the distribution of airphotos.
Provides technical supervision of all photo interpreters in the theater army, including recommendations for training objectives and policies.

Weather section.
Obtains weather forecasts of the operational area and detailed upper air analysis as required for available weapons systems.
Prepares data on climate and weather.

ADMINISTRATIVE BRANCH

Chief, administrative branch.
Prepares duty and staff visit rosters for the entire intelligence division.

Message center.
Maintains the division message center, journal, and journal file.
Routes all incoming material for action or information.

Library and central files.
Maintains library of source and reference material, control files and records, for use of the intelligence division.
Establishes TOP SECRET control procedures for the intelligence division.

Personnel, supply, and fiscal section.
Determines requirements for, procures, distributes, and documents intelligence personnel, supplies, and funds.
Assigns office space and performs housekeeping tasks for the intelligence division.
Prepares all personnel reports for the intelligence division.

Publications section.
Reproduces, edits, and assembles all intelligence division publications and makes bulk distribution.

Committee and liaison section.
Coordinates activities of intelligence liaison personnel and provides liaison officers to higher, lower, and adjacent headquarters.
Provides signal communications, transportation, etc., for liaison officers.
Provides representatives on committees requiring intelligence participation and clerical and other administrative assistance such members.
Prepares and distributes reports of liaison and committee activities.

Figure 46C. Intelligence section, theater army headquarters—reconnaissance and mapping branch and administrative branch.

INDEX

241

Drones, 138
Duds, 121

E

ECCM, 87
ECM, 87
EEI, 65, 212-218
Electronic intelligence, 5
Electronic warfare, 87
Electronic warfare units, 20
Enemy
  Air capability, 200
  Capabilities, 202, 206-211
  CBR, 90, 200
  Committed forces, 196
  Composition, 190
  Defense, 215
  Delaying action, 215
  EW, 89
  Information, 59
  Order of battle, 217
  Peculiarities and weaknesses, 201
  Reinforcements, 199, 215
  Signal communications, 120
  Situation map, 41
  Strength, 196
  Tactical nuclear capability, 216
  Vulnerability, 205, 217
  Withdrawal, 215
Escape, 84
Essential elements of information, 65,
  212-218
Estimate, intelligence, 55, 189-205
Evaluation, 43
Evasion, 84
EW, 87
Examples
  Annex, 226
  Area of operations analysis, 165-170
  Climatic summary, 149
  Collection worksheet, 222, 223
  Estimate, 191-195
  Interpretation, 48
  ISUM, 156, 157
  Nuclear burst report, 145
  Operation of cycle, 8
  PERINTREP, 160
  Shelrep, 144

F

Fallout, 33
Fallout predictions, 153
FBI, 110
Federal Bureau of Investigation, 110
Field use, EW, 88

Files, intelligence, 43
Fire, 172
Flexibility, 13
Fragments, missile and shell, 121
Frontier security, 76

G

General war, 96
Ground surveillance radar, 135
Guerrilla warfare, 84
Guerrillas, 20

H

Humidity, 185

I

Imagination, 13
Importance, intelligence, 1
Influence of weather, 179-182
Infrared devices, 30
Integration, 47
Intelligence
  Annex, 71, 224-227
  Collection, 17-37
  Combat, 3
  Combined operations, 96
  Communications, 5
  Counterintelligence, 5, 73-81, 228,
    229
  Cycle, 6
  Definition, 2
  Dissemination, 50-57, 151-155
  Electronic, 5
  Estimate, 55, 79, 189-205
  Evaluation, 43
  Files, 43
  Flexibility, 13
  General war, 96
  Importance, 1
  Joint operations, 97
  Journal, 41
  Limited war, 95
  Maps, 154
  National, 2
  Nuclear warfare, 93
  Officer, 100
  Operations, 11
  Order of battle, 5, 111-114
  Planning, 13, 58-72, 79
  Principles, 6
  Processing, 38-49
  Responsibilities, 99
  Situations short of war, 94
  Special operations, 82-92
  Staff organization, 101, 233-240

244   COMBAT INTELLIGENCE IN MODERN WARFARE

S

Scale, map, 155
Scope of effort, EW, 89
Security, 14
Security agency units, 20
Security company, 125
Security units, 74
Severe weather warnings, 147
Shell fragments, 121
Shell reports, 121
Situations short of war, 94
Soldier as counterintelligence agent, 74
Sources of information, 17, 117-123
Special forces, 20
Special operations, 76, 82-92
Specific search, 26
Spies, 20
Spot report, 51
Staff organization, G2, 101
Staffs, intelligence, 233-240
    Division, 233
    Field army, 234, 235
    Logistical command, 236, 237
    Theater army, 238-240
Standard report, (shell, bomb, mortar, toxic, nuclear), 143
Stay-behind units, 20
Strategic intelligence, 3
Strength, 111
Summary, intelligence, 51, 156, 157
Supervision of collecting, 71
Support of close combat forces, 209
Surveillance, combat, 32
Surveillance plan, 139

T

TAC request form, 131
Tactical air force, 30
Tactical cover, 85
Tactical use of radar, 140
Tactics, 112
Target acquisition, 63
Technical intelligence, 5, 115, 116
Technical intelligence bulletins and summaries, 152

Technical intelligence detachments, 20
Technical services, 21
Temperature, 183
Terrain, 185
Terrain conditions, 218
Theater counterintelligence, 78
Time factor in committing troops, 209
Timely intelligence, 9
Toxic agents, 90
Training, 104
Travel security, 76

U

Unconventional warfare, 83
United States Intelligence Board, 109
Unit history, 114
Unit identification, 111
Useful intelligence, 9
Use of intelligence, 50-57

V

Visibility, 183

W

Weather, 63
Weather conditions, 171
Weather, effects on
    Equipment and supplies, 179
    Manmade features, 180
    Natural features, 180
    Nuclear weapons, 183-188
    Personnel, 179
    Special equipment, 182
    Tactical activities, 180
    Weapons, 182
Weather forecast, 147
Weather information, 122
Weather intelligence, 146-150
Weather reconnaissance, 29
Weather summary, 146
Wind, 185
Worksheet, collection, 70
Worksheet, counterintelligence, 80
Worksheet, G2, 42